Contents

Acknowledgements

There are many people to thank. Without those who came to the patients' focus groups and the NHS managers and clinicians who attended other focus groups, we would not have obtained such a proper appreciation of how staff and patients experienced the existing Charter. Without the organisations whose representatives contributed to the written evidence and the in-depth interviews, we would have been unable to appreciate the many different perspectives of the Charter quality issues in the NHS. To all these people we would like to express our gratitude.

We also wish to thank:

Penny Banks, Mark Duman, Alison Forbes, Steve Manning, Bob Sang and Ian Wylie from the King's Fund who helped put the original brief together, offering support and helpful comments throughout, as well as Jan Stokes-Carter, who recruited people for the managers' and clinicians' focus group.

Social and Community Planning Research (SCPR) for recruiting patients and running the focus groups, particularly Jill Keegan.

Lucy Johnson, King's Fund Library, for assistance in identifying sources for the literature review.

Janet Hadley for editing the report, Pat Tawn for masterly report design and typing, and last, but not least, the NHS Executive and the King's Fund for providing the money for the work.

Christine Farrell, programme director at the King's Fund
Ros Levenson, independent consultant and visiting fellow at the King's Fund
Dawn Snape, research director at Social and Community Planning Research (SCPR)

The Patient's Charter

Past and future

Christine Farrell, Ros Levenson, Dawn Snape

Published by
King's Fund Publishing
11–13 Cavendish Square
London W1M 0AN

First published 1998

ISBN 1 85717 216 7
A CIP catalogue record for this book is available from the British Library

Available from:
King's Fund Bookshop
11–13 Cavendish Square
London W1M 0AN
Tel: 0171 307 2591

Printed and bound in Great Britain

Cover illustration by Minuche Mazumdar Farrar

Preface

The Labour Party's Election Manifesto (1997) contained a commitment to reviewing the Patient's Charter and to producing a new one. The King's Fund had been planning a piece of research on the Charter in the spring of 1997 and when the Government's review was formally announced later that summer they were commissioned by the NHS Executive to carry it out.

The aim of the research was to review the workings of the Patient's Charter from the point of view of patients, carers, and NHS workers (managers and clinicians). As well as considering views and experiences of how the Charter has worked in the past, the main focus was on its purpose in the future: that is, the Charter philosophy, the rights and responsibilities of the state provider and the citizen, areas and aspects of services, and service delivery to be covered.

The study was designed as a five-stage process starting with a review of the literature and moving through in-depth interviews with patient organisations, focus groups with patients, NHS managers and clinicians, written evidence from a sample of NHS trusts, community health councils, royal colleges, professional organisations and voluntary organisations and, finally, in-depth interviews with representatives of vulnerable sections of society, such as homeless people, refugees, minority ethnic groups and people with disabilities. This process allowed us to build the findings from the first stage into the design of the second, and so on. We were thus able to check the extent of agreement or disagreement about the findings from one stage with the next. The research began in September 1997 and was completed in February 1998.

The research findings were presented to the Government's Advisory Group on the Patient's Charter, chaired by Greg Dyke, in February 1998. After this presentation, the Group asked the King's Fund to do two more pieces of work. The first, to run a series of discussions with Advisory Group members, to use their expertise to develop relevant Charter standards. The second, to take the research findings and the results of the Advisory Group's deliberations back to the original focus groups' participants, to ask for their views on standards and their implementation. This work was completed in May 1998 and reported to the Advisory Group in June.

The report is in six parts. The first part is the *main report* which draws together the findings of the research and makes recommendations. It is followed by five appendices. The first four are detailed reports of the findings of the separate parts of the research. Appendix 5 is an account of the research methods and the people who participated.

Summary

Consensus for a new charter

The existing Patient's Charter has a contentious public reputation. Despite this, there is a remarkable and reassuring level of agreement between the different groups which took part in the research reported here.

If a new Patient's Charter were drawn up solely by patients it would have much in common with the concerns of NHS staff but would also reflect differences of emphasis, particularly on the need for advocacy and information to enable people to make best use of the NHS. Comments from patients and staff on the current Charter also overlap: the main report reveals differences of emphasis only in the details.

Advantages of the existing Charter

- Has raised staff awareness of patients' needs, issues and rights
- Helped set standards and identify priorities for action
- Set comparable standards for reviews of performance
- Helped to move NHS culture towards a 'user perspective'

Disadvantages of the existing Charter

- Lack of clarity about its aim – this engendered wide scepticism
- Not enough user or staff involvement in creating the document
- Too much emphasis on quantitative standards
- Ignores clinical standards and outcomes
- Some standards irrelevant to patients' real needs, especially those of vulnerable people
- Hard to monitor – data costly to collect and sometimes fudged and/or ignored
- Hospital services dominate at expense of primary care
- Low patient awareness of Charter
- Patients' expectations unrealistically raised
- Little emphasis on patients' responsibilities

A new NHS Charter should contain:

- an unambiguous statement about its aims and values
- principles of openness, accountability and equity

- a much stronger focus on primary and community care
- a wider and clearer statement of patients' rights of access to services
- wider standards which focus on quality of service:
  – for clinical need, effectiveness, and outcomes
  – for equity and access to services/treatment
  – for the quality of the patient experience
  – for better communication and information in a usable form
- emphasise not only patients' rights but also their responsibilities and foster ways of encouraging such behaviour
- better publicity for the Charter
- regular reviews of the content and impact of the Charter.

The process of creating this document must involve *patients and staff*. Better monitoring and feedback systems are essential to inform staff and patients about progress and standards achieved.

There is no substitute for a national charter, but local charters can be useful, provided they are based on consultation and create standards relevant to local conditions.

PART 1: RESEARCH FINDINGS AND RECOMMENDATIONS

Introduction

> *The Patient's Charter is one of those topics that elicit a response when mentioned; people either like it or they do not, but they are rarely indifferent to it.* (Tschudin 1997)

Ever since the Patient's Charter was launched in October 1991 it has been the subject of sustained argument. Are the contents appropriate? Does it provide a means to better services? Does it encourage unrealistic expectations, or empower patients to get the best from the NHS? Does it make any difference at all, and is a patient's charter an effective tool for improving quality in the NHS? These are the kinds of questions that managers, clinicians, patients and carers ask, although they sometimes arrive at different answers.

The change of government and the greater emphasis on openness and accountability has provided an opportunity to re-visit some of the concerns of both patients and staff about the NHS. As the Prime Minister, Tony Blair, wrote in the foreword to a book about the NHS:

> *The NHS touches every one of us and it is particularly appropriate that we should reflect on this in the 50th anniversary year of our National Health Service, while taking time to consider the opportunities for its future.* (Rivett 1998)

Reviewing the Patient's Charter is just one aspect of considering those opportunities for the future. However, although the existing Charter is undoubtedly flawed and constraining, it has many aspects which can be developed.

The NHS exists for patients and the quality of NHS services for those who use it must be at the heart of any review of the Charter. However, in order to be truly effective, a charter must address the needs of potential patients as well as actual patients and their carers. Some sections of the community still have considerable problems of access to the NHS. There are also major inequalities in health status and health care across the country. The Green Paper, *Our Healthier Nation* (1998), acknowledges that poor health has complex causes and recognises that health inequalities are widening. Unless these inequalities are tackled and a collaborative approach is used that transcends bureaucratic and organisational boundaries, the development of the NHS will be limited.

Although the Patient's Charter is only a small 'tool' for change and for moving towards an NHS system which works to redress inequalities, it does have a part to play in the government's overall strategy.

It is also important that the needs and views of all staff in the NHS are taken into account. While there has been an increased awareness of the significance of clinical expertise from doctors and from nurses, other groups of staff must not be overlooked. Porters, administrative staff, technicians, managers and many others are all part of the NHS, and a charter and any other tools for improving it must take into account their concerns and build on their experiences.

The White Paper, *The New NHS: Modern – Dependable* (1997), stresses the modernisation of the NHS to prepare it for the next 50 years. It explicitly describes a modern NHS as providing information and services at home, in the community and in hospital. It also emphasises primary care as a driving force within the NHS. Any considerations of the Patient's Charter must reflect these priorities.

What are the purposes of a charter in the NHS?

The changes that are signalled by the White Paper and by the Green Paper make a fresh look at the Patient's Charter timely and appropriate. The Patient's Charter says that it is helping the NHS to:

- listen to and act on people's views and needs
- set clear standards of service
- provide services which meet those standards.

What sort of charter would be most effective in helping the NHS deliver a service? While different approaches are here considered in turn, it is possible to combine several approaches in one document if there is sufficient clarity about them and their aims.

A codification of rights

In the literature review (Appendix 1) and to a lesser extent in the patients' focus groups (Appendix 4), the Patient's Charter has been criticised because the extent to which it is a document of rights is unclear. It draws a distinction between rights and expectations in the following terms:

Rights – which all patients will receive all the time
Expectations – standards of service which the NHS is aiming to achieve. Exceptional circumstances may sometimes prevent these standards being met.

We found that the Patient's Charter created confusion about rights and expectations. The rationale for what was a right and what was an expectation, and the differential monitoring of standards may have clouded the purposes of the Charter as a whole.

One view, expressed by patients in the focus groups, is that a new charter should codify the rights of those who use the NHS. The literature also argues for a firmer base in social rights (Bynoe 1996), while other writers express a preference for a Bill of Rights (Thain 1992). A rights-based charter would emphasise those aspects of the NHS to which there was a clear and enforceable right but the prospect of producing an accurate document of manageable size would be enough to daunt the most capable of writers. This also raises the question of the practice rather than the theory of rights. While there is a clear right for everyone to be registered with a GP, we know that enforcing it is far from simple, especially for those who do not speak English or who are homeless.

Setting minimum standards

A charter might also set minimum standards. While this is close to the rights approach, it is not so legalistic. It tends to be pragmatic rather than principled and to define a level of service which can be delivered and where one could reasonably expect redress if it were not. This seems to have been influential regarding the expectations which the Patient's Charter described. Typically, documents which set minimum standards obviously concentrate on areas where there has been concern about them in the past. Long waits for operations was a pressing issue when the Charter was being devised and, as we shall see later in the section on setting and monitoring standards, this approach did not deal adequately with patient and staff concerns.

While some people have criticised the impact of defining minimum standards, others have welcomed the fact that the Charter has raised the awareness of both the public and NHS staff about quality issues and standards.

Setting aspirational standards

A charter can also set standards which indicate the direction and speed of travel towards improved service standards and expectations in the Patient's Charter reflect this approach. Aspirational standards are not so much a framework for monitoring current standards as an exhortation to make improvements. An aspirational charter can bring services in line with overall strategy, or it can apply pressure where performance has been unsatisfactory.

Aspirational standards can encourage and empower patients to press for improvements and clearer rights, but can also put unremitting pressure on those who deliver services. It is hardly surprising that opinions on aspirational standards reflect diverse patient and staff roles. However patients and health advocates say that aspirational standards can sometimes obscure the actual reality of services in favour of a utopian view of the NHS.

A management tool

The Charter has been called a *patient's* charter (our emphasis) but in fact it has been a charter about what patients can expect as much as a charter for them to use, with its primary function being a vehicle for managers to improve standards. Some patients, however, have used it to obtain better services or to learn what they can expect from the NHS.

Staff feel that a significant impact of the Charter has been to concentrate their minds on centrally defined priorities for action. Appendices 3 and 4 show that managers and clinicians are sometimes ambivalent about whether this has helped them improve services. The literature review (Allen 1995, Cohen 1994) and the interviews with voluntary organisations and patients' groups also show widespread criticisms of aspects of services that were chosen for the Patient's Charter, and the means by which particular rights and standards were selected. However, there seems to be agreement that the Charter did focus the minds of both managers and clinicians on how to make changes in certain parts of the service which benefited patients.

The 1983 management review conducted by Roy Griffiths identified the need for a general manager at each level, regardless of discipline. The introduction of general management was supposed to give NHS managers a clearly defined function and the power to enable integrated change to take place in line with agreed strategies, managers found they often lacked a framework for improving standards and performance. The Patient's Charter may have helped to provide this framework.

Defining what the NHS can and cannot do

A charter may set out not only minimum standards in respect of particular aspects of the service, but may also indicate what one might expect of the NHS in broad terms. It may try to define the core business of the NHS, or particular services within the NHS. While the Patient's Charter has not yet travelled far along this route, it is certainly a new direction that could be developed for a charter, if debates about prioritisation are more public, as the focus groups have suggested.

A statement of values

A charter can also make statements about the values of a service, and try to clarify the philosophy behind it. This is less precise than the rights orientation described above or the setting of minimum standards. Comments in the Patient's Charter about respect for privacy, dignity and religious and cultural beliefs are an attempt to make a statement about values and ethos. These expectations are located in the 'Personal Consideration and Respect' section, where the Charter includes a statement about rights (to choose whether to take part in medical research or medical student training), a section on expected standards (staff wearing name badges) and a section on values and ethos (privacy, dignity and respect for religious and cultural beliefs.)

While a statement of values can be about services generally rather than specifically, it can also be the foundation for real improvements in a service. Core values can also define the national benchmark as the foundation for genuinely local work to steer local action into line with national priorities, but at the same time reflecting local needs and circumstances. While some users and organisations favour detailed and specific standards, there is also considerable support for a clear statement of values.

Towards a new charter

The time now is right for the government to consider what it aims to achieve through a new NHS charter. While all the points discussed here have their merits, a new charter needs to go beyond the limitations of them all. It should stimulate change, but not produce expectations remote from what is practical. It should include a clear statement of aims and how it can contribute to the delivery of quality services in the NHS. Staff and patients clearly need to be involved in writing it and regular reviews of its content and impact must also involve all who use and serve the NHS.

Our research suggests it should reflect a number of fundamental principles. These are:

- openness and accountability
- equity or fairness
- partnerships between patients and NHS staff
- access to services on the basis of clinical need
- consideration for vulnerable groups and their access to services
- user and staff involvement.

Perceptions and experiences of the Patient's Charter

Patients asked about the Charter said they had heard about it but were not familiar with its contents. In fact, they usually had some knowledge of it and what it was about and could, when pushed, guess at its content, but they lacked a clear understanding of it overall. This corresponds with existing survey conclusions (NOP 1994) and confirms findings in France and Finland – the only other Western countries which have health charters. (Bourgine P. 1984; Tugend & Harris, 1997)

None of the patients in the focus groups had seen a copy of the Patient's Charter but they did remember references to it in the press or at their local hospitals. They also felt that the intention of the Charter might be:

- to improve NHS service quality and choice
- to demonstrate performance against targets
- to ensure fairer distribution of resources by setting a framework of patients' rights, regardless of where they lived or their ability to pay
- to give patients the right to complain or ask questions if they felt their rights had been infringed
- to provide a means of monitoring the service.

Scepticism about the Charter was evident in all areas of the research. The literature review found several sources which commented on its 'political taint'. Patient organisations and voluntary groups hinted at 'political manipulation'. Representatives of vulnerable groups were particularly sceptical and emphasised the lack of awareness among the people whom they represented. Once these reservations had been made known, however, everyone was happy to move on and discuss the positive contribution the Charter had made to NHS services and patients' use of them.

Experiences of the Charter

The overwhelming view of the Charter among those who had experience of it was that it had limited usefulness. Most people acknowledged positive aspects to it but these views were expressed much less enthusiastically than those concerned with its weaknesses.

Strengths of the Charter

The literature review offered limited perspective on the usefulness or strengths of the charter and these can be summarised as: informing patients about the standards they could reasonably expect (NOP 1994); and the effect on day-to-day running of hospitals in terms of helping patients to identify failures in the standards of services (Tailor & Mayberry 1995).

Our research with voluntary organisations and patient groups identified three main strengths of the Charter. That it had:

- raised awareness among NHS staff of patient needs, issues and rights
- helped to set standards and identify priorities for action
- set standards for performance which allowed comparisons and reviews of performance.

Interviews with representatives of vulnerable groups showed that the Patient's Charter had been important because it had set out rights and expectations. Inside the NHS, staff commented on its value in stimulating debates about standards and offering basic, minimum targets which must be met and improved. Perhaps the most important point made by NHS staff was that the raising of awareness of patients' needs and experiences had helped change the culture towards a user perspective.

Weaknesses of the Charter

Everyone agreed on the weaknesses of the Charter and pointed out what it did *not* do as much as what the difficulties were to which it had given rise. Chart 1 illustrates the major weaknesses identified.

Chart 1 Weaknesses of the Patient's Charter

Problems with standards and rights

- Lack of clarity
- Too much emphasis on quantitative (waiting times) standards and not enough attention to quality standards
- Ignores clinical standards/need/outcomes

Difficulties with monitoring

- Uncoordinated, incompetent data-collection systems
- Extra work in collecting data
- Unreliable statistics
- Lack of clear definition of standards which complicates monitoring

Raised patients' expectations too high

- Expectations raised beyond the resources of services
- No patient responsibilities included

Problems with standards and rights

The lack of clarity in the existing charter and the confusion between 'rights' and 'standards' were points much commented upon in the literature (Hogg 1994, Carr Hill & Ng 1992, Bynoe 1996). Criticisms of the way the Charter concentrated on acute services and on quantitative aspects of services were even more pronounced (Lorentzon 1996, Cohen 1994, Benton 1993). All our evidence supports these criticisms. The relative neglect of non-acute services was a point often raised, particularly in relation to people with long-term conditions, the mentally ill and other groups whose care is offered in community and primary care settings. NHS staff in the focus groups reinforced these views.

> *It [the Patient's Charter] never actually looked at the care and it was never meant to look at the care and I think that was most frustrating to clinicians because … from a clinicians' point of view it wasn't measuring what we perceived to be quality.*
>
> Clinician

Specific issues were raised, such as the way charter standards had 'distorted' the good management of care by focusing on one part of the system while neglecting others but the primary concern was the way charter standards had led to prioritisation by time rather than clinical need.

Very few people are going to come to any great harm if they don't have their varicose veins done, and yet they could be displacing more worthwhile – dare I say it – procedures. So that's a kind of meaningless [standard], just having a crude policy that nobody must wait more than ... 18 months.

Clinician

Difficulties with monitoring

NHS managers expressed particular concern about charter monitoring systems and methods. Their criticisms fell into four main categories:

- inadequate infrastructure to support monitoring
- difficulties with the reliability of the data produced
- inadequate tools to measure quality
- inadequate feedback mechanisms from results to performance review.

Our trust didn't have sophisticated information technology and so to capture a 30 minutes wait in outpatients, it was all written down by hand on a little form. We had to devise a form and the nurses had to write down the time they arrived, time of appointment, and time of departure. That, in itself, could be open to abuse of course, but it was that kind of thing, because we didn't have the infrastructure to capture it in any other way ...

Manager

Another recurrent theme was a feeling that the statistics produced did not reflect what actually happened (Friend 1995, Hart 1996). Managers questioned the reliability of the data because of staff failure to give priority to monitoring, due to pressure of work, and inadequate tools for measurement of quality standards like privacy and dignity of patients. Some also expressed frustration that when they did make attempts to record the required statistics, little use was made of them internally.

I once put extra time and effort into looking at precisely where the problems [with trolley waits] were ... [but] nobody was interested anyway. So we've just resorted to the minimum data collection we can possibly attempt now.

Clinician

Raised expectations

The most interesting category of complaints expressed concern about the rise in patient expectations. Managers and clinicians, especially general practitioners, felt this had put extra pressure on them at a time when resources were not available to meet them. Yet it is difficult to reconcile this pressure given the low patient awareness of the Charter.

In the minds of some NHS staff, the Charter ignored patient responsibilities, putting all the onus on staff. Some people believed this 'bias' in the Charter was connected to the rise they had experienced in aggression.

> *It's all very one-sided and patients, particularly relatives, have become very aggressive towards nursing staff ...*
>
> Clinician

Added to this was a definite feeling among staff that the Charter encouraged people to complain.

> *A lot of people feel there is a focus on complaining rather than commenting or complementing and a lot of staff feel that patients are almost encouraged to complain.*
>
> Clinician

Yet comments from patient organisations suggested that the Charter named irrelevant rights and that as far as primary care services were concerned, the new complaints system was a failure.

These are areas where patient and staff perceptions and experiences were widely different. Ways of resolving such discrepancies surely need to be considered.

To summarise, the difficulties which managers and clinicians experienced with the Charter were specific and detailed and the limited gains it had introduced did not compensate for this. Yet, while patient organisations identified similar difficulties and limited virtues, patients themselves did not see the Charter as an important part of their NHS experiences. Patient's concerns were with the services themselves, their access to them, and the way they were treated when they had to use them.

National and local charters

It is hard to know how many and what kind of local charters have been developed. Carr, Hill & Ng (1992) examined local charters from 140 health authorities and 50 family health service authorities. They found that only a third (30 per cent) separated national and local standards. We asked a specific question to address this issue. Five main concerns were identified:

- a national charter is essential to maintain the NHS as a *national* service with national standards
- only a national charter can ensure the principle of equity in the NHS
- local charters are important to set standards relevant to local circumstances
- local charters should involve all key stakeholders (staff, patients, carers, and commissioners) in their development to ensure effective ownership and implementation
- the problem of confusion between national and local charter standards could be avoided by introducing a national framework which should be mirrored and built upon by local charters.

There was considerable support for this last proposal. It was seen to set local standards within the context of local priorities and resources. More importantly, it would maintain national standards (and equity) while allowing local people to be involved in the development of local standards.

Worries were expressed about a proliferation of standards causing confusion in the minds of patients and the public. Nevertheless, the desire to maintain national standards with local conditions gained almost universal approval.

Progress towards this position may be slow if good outcomes are required. As McIver and Martin noted:

> *The key to producing local charters is to develop them with service users so that standards relate to aspects of the service they consider important.*
>
> (McIver & Martin 1996)

The process of involving users and staff will take time and need careful handling and there may be competing interests, not all of which can be served. But if the national framework can offer a model acceptable to the majority of staff, patients and carers, that process will be a means not only of producing a local charter, but also of educating NHS staff and patients and helping all stakeholders in health to understand one another. This in turn should help to develop the patient partnership so clearly desired by many staff.

Setting and monitoring standards

Here, we consider some of the issues involved in setting and monitoring standards that have emerged from the various components of the research.

Standards should relate to clinical need and should be evidence-based

Much of the concern focused on the particular standards selected for the Patient's Charter, rather than with the principle of defining standards generally in a charter, for which there was qualified support. As one person said:

> *Who in their right mind could possibly argue against these kinds of standards when previously there were none at all and there was no frame of reference for patients to assess whether or not the waiting time was excessive or against the rules?* (Ryland 1996)

Similarly, some patients' groups felt that it was helpful to define rights and standards to ensure an appropriate level and quality of service delivery.

There was widespread concern among staff about the factors responsible for reducing waiting times. The drive to meet Patient's Charter standards was sometimes seen as a pressure to overlook clinical need.

> *Surely the priority of the day is determined on the basis of clinical need of each patient who comes in, and I think the Charter has actually interfered with that to a certain extent.*
>
> Clinician

> *Many of the standards do not focus on clinical need but on something else, e.g. time waited. Also the standards work against each other, for example. 12 to 18 months waited versus cancelled operations.*
>
> Health authority

There were fears that reductions in waiting times for certain treatments might increase waiting times for others. Research showed that patients criticised a system that dealt with long waits for hospital admission without providing extra resources to make a genuine difference overall. Staff were no less critical and the Patient's Charter was described as:

> *A bludgeon to beat staff with when the real problem is resourcing but a useful means of exerting pressure [as a patient]* (Viewpoint Readers' Panel 1995. Nursing Standard)

Benton (1993) noted that most of the measures applied in the Patient's Charter are either process or *output* oriented and not *outcome* oriented. We found that both patients and staff expressed concerns about standards which concentrated on process rather than outcome. For example, we heard from several sources that patients may be assessed in accident and emergency departments within five minutes, they may then wait several hours for treatment. The 'hello nurse' has become symbolic of the triumph of process over outcome, and of the ability of 'coal-face' staff to subvert top-down policy if it is thought to be of little relevance to real life.

Our interviews confirmed the suggestion in the literature (Lorentzon 1996) that from the patient's point of view, long waits in outpatients may not be the most important aspect of the outpatient experience. Long waiting times are not related to the severity of the patient's clinical condition. Patients also stressed the need for appropriate standards for primary care, pointing out that the most prominent Patient's Charter standards related mostly to acute hospital care.

Lack of a strategic framework

We found little evidence that Patient's Charter standards have enabled, or encouraged, a strategic approach to improving services for patients. Much cynicism pervaded the research findings from all sources, as the Patient's Charter was felt to be a mixed bag of short-term imperatives rather than long-term policy for improvement and change.

A related point concerned the division of a whole system into discrete parts for setting service standards and monitoring. Staff in the focus groups felt that standards about waits on trolleys in accident and emergency needed to become part of a wider system of bed management. Carers were concerned that standards aimed at faster throughput in hospital might overlook the requirements of carers as well as failing to fulfil the needs of patients.

Quality

There was much concern about the impact of the Charter on quality. People often said the Patient's Charter concentrated on aspects of quality that did not adequately reflect patients' concerns or experiences. It was seen to concentrate on access to services but in a narrow sense, such as waiting times. There was also undue emphasis on aspects of quality that could be quantified:

> *Quantitative indicators are nearly always seized upon because they measure that which is measurable, rather than that which is significant.* (Hart 1996)

The same sentiment emerged in the focus groups.

> *It felt like a political move, so that the government could demonstrate some form of quality going on in a service which didn't necessarily reflect the real issues on the ground as far as quality was concerned.*
>
> Manager

The Charter was viewed positively as a vehicle for considering issues of quality, including aspects that were broader than those rights and standards it contained. Other responses were highly critical of the contribution the Charter made to quality. Interviews with patients' organisations and specialist groups and the literature review indicate that patients take a fairly dim view of the Charter's impact on quality. Most of the positive comments were about the benefits, in broad terms, of *attempting* to set out rights and standards, rather than about specific quality improvements as a result of its implementation.

Patients value aspects of quality that are difficult to quantify, such as a positive staff attitude, friendliness and dignity. They are also keenly interested in the quality of the outcome of their actual health care intervention, including whether they are treated by professionals with appropriate qualifications and competence, and whether or not they were kept as free as possible from pain and indignity. The quality of information also matters a great deal to patients and is discussed further below. The environment within which care is delivered is also important for some patients and managers, although it does not appear prominently as a Patient's Charter standard.

Interviews with organisations which were particularly concerned about access to the NHS, such as homeless people and refugees, indicated that the kinds of quality issues to which the Patient's Charter had given greatest attention were perhaps irrelevant for some patients, since they lack basic access to services in the first place. Thus, for homeless people, a waiting list based on contact with a patient at a permanent home address was doomed to fail whatever the length of the waiting time. Or, for the health advocate who was advised not to inform a non-English speaking patient about GP services (because of the service's inability to communicate with the patient), Patient's Charter notions of quality in, for example, the speed of transfer of medical records to a new GP are somewhat meaningless.

Written evidence indicates the following six main categories as the most important for quality standards:

- clinical effectiveness
- access to services/treatment
- user involvement/partnerships
- effective information/communication
- staff training/qualifications and behaviour
- general aspects of care, including privacy, dignity and respect.

Monitoring standards

There was also much general concern about how the Patient's Charter was monitored. The emphasis within quality on quantifiable standards was reflected in monitoring procedures.

There has been enormous pressure on staff to conform to the strictures of the Patient's Charter and this can lead to distortions in data collection or presentation. In its worst manifestation, Friend (1995) reports allegations that nurses have been threatened by disciplinary action if they do not meet Charter targets. The focus groups revealed a Charter-related culture of blame which did little or nothing to improve services.

Many patients and their organisations appear to be aware of these factors – and, to some extent, the credibility of the Charter has been undermined. However, taking the interviews as a whole, patients and their organisations had many constructive suggestions for monitoring quality in a more realistic way, including the use of:

- focus groups to listen to patients' views
- market research techniques to survey patients' views

- on-going panels of regular users to ascertain patients' views over time
- opportunistic surveys and discussions in waiting areas
- publication of local qualitative studies
- inspections by outside independent bodies
- expanded role for community health councils (CHCs).

Patients with long-term conditions who are regular users of the NHS are often keen, well informed and able to supplement numerical data with genuine personal experience of how services are working in practice. They usually appreciate the research but are suspicious of anything that resembles a box-ticking approach to performance management.

Performance league tables were seen by many staff and patients as simplistic or misleading. Staff also felt they were a temptation to be less than honest about the realities of the service. Focus groups with staff confirmed evidence in the literature and from patients in indicating that 'unsatisfactory' figures might be unacceptable and sent back by managers for revision, with no genuine alteration to the service in question.

The Association of Community Health Councils for England and Wales (ACHCEW) proposed an independent Health Rights Commission to monitor patient's rights and ensure that they are implemented. Other organisations and individual patients express their willingness and enthusiasm to be seen as part of a regular and ongoing quality monitoring mechanism. Focus groups also suggested greater involvement of CHCs and patients in monitoring.

Information and the Patient's Charter

Information for patients and staff is recognised as central to the effective use and provision of NHS services. The Audit Commission pointed out in 1993 that information and communication were particularly important to users of the service and its report identified poor communication as a primary source of dissatisfaction. Although the present Patient's Charter includes a section on the right to information of certain kinds, there is still concern about the lack of communication in the NHS. Other commentators (LeTouze 1997, Rigge 1997) have noted patients' and users' need for information and that it is sometimes unavailable or difficult to obtain. Our research confirms the importance patients, carers, and NHS staff attach to good information and communication.

The existing Patient's Charter includes the right to information about conditions and treatments clearly explained before a patient decides whether to agree to it, which includes any risks involved in those treatments; access to a patient's own records in most circumstances; detailed information on local services and a prompt investigation of, and a full reply to, any complaint about NHS services. While this kind of information is generally welcomed by patients, each of these 'rights' is limited in some way. Patients themselves felt the following were important:

- information about conditions, treatments, medications with risks and benefits clearly explained
- information about NHS services available and how to access them
- information about standards of NHS services
- information about non-NHS support services.

Information about clinical conditions, diagnoses, treatment, and alternatives

When asked what kind of information was most useful to people using NHS services, two-thirds of staff identified as *the* most important clinical information about individual conditions and treatments; the risks and benefits of treatments and medications.

> *If they are to be informed partners in their own health care, patients need clinical information; for example what tests are being carried out, why, and their results; why a certain intervention has been chosen or drugs have been prescribed and how they will work; on rehabilitation care and on what is expected of them and why.*
>
> Manager

Patients in the focus groups also felt information about conditions and treatments was important because this helped them feel more in control of what was happening to them and less anxious.

Information on local services

The evidence indicates that information about the standards of local services and what to expect of them was also highly important. Access to, and use of, local services is obviously dependent on the availability of good information. Patients felt that without it they were unable to exercise any of the rights which the Charter had given them. Representatives of vulnerable groups pointed out that without this kind of information, published in minority languages and/or appearing in places where people such as the homeless and refugees had access to it, use of any NHS service was difficult or inappropriate. This contention is supported by Tailor and Mayberry's study (1995) which reports that only 42 per cent of people were aware of their right to receive detailed information on local health services.

In the written evidence, where respondents were specifically asked about the need for information, access to services was identified as the second most important category.

> *First, people need information about how to access the NHS in an emergency or for routine care. As suggested in the Chief Medical Officers' Review of Emergency Care in the Community, they may need information to assist them in judging the nature and severity of their condition in order that they can make an informed decision about how to access the services.*
>
> Ambulance trust

> *Information on what can realistically be expected within any given health situation. More comprehensive information to members of the public of services available in districts would enable them to make choices.*
>
> Community & mental health trust

Information about non-NHS services, particularly voluntary organisations and self-help groups, was another category of information ranked as useful. The importance of information about local social services was mentioned by organisations for people with long-term medical conditions and vulnerable groups.

Information about standards of NHS services

Patients wanted facts about the quality of care and NHS staff said they were keen to help them understand more about the clinical performance of local NHS services, especially those which might assist them in making better choices about doctors. Patients wanted this, too, but felt that they were forced to rely upon the quality assurance systems within the NHS to ensure that any clinician would perform to a high standard.

Information about complaints procedures

Tailor and Mayberry (1995) reported that only 44 per cent of people knew about the right to have any complaint about the NHS investigated. We also found many reasons why patients are unwilling to complain, irrespective of whether or not they know their rights.

At the most basic level, patients fear – sometimes with good reason – that if they complain about a GP they will be removed from that GP's list. Many other factors, such as gratitude and a general unwillingness to criticise staff who are working under pressure, also inhibit complaints. Staff also said they felt patients did not wish to complain and gave several reasons why this might be so. There is, however, a widespread feeling that the Patient's Charter has made patients more likely to complain.

Information matters

Patients and NHS staff have information requirements far wider than the Patient's Charter specifies and it is clear that even more information is required to enable patients to make use of their existing rights. For example, the Charter mentions a right to be referred to a consultant who is acceptable to the patient, but it is difficult for a patient (and sometimes also difficult for the referring doctor) to obtain current information on the most suitable specialist.

The issue is about information rather than a matter of just wanting facts. It is about needing a wider range of factual information, of receiving it in a usable form at an appropriate time and, perhaps most important of all, with a friendly and encouraging delivery, so that the patient can put it to good use.

Access to services

In a limited way, the Patient's Charter made a serious attempt to improve patients' access to the NHS. It set out the right to receive health care on the basis of clinical need and not on ability to pay, or on lifestyle or any other factor.

It also stated that a patient has a right to:

- register with a GP
- change their GP easily and quickly
- get emergency medical treatment

- be referred to a consultant who was acceptable to the patient when the GP thinks it necessary
- be referred for a second opinion if the patient and GP agreed that it was desirable.

The Patient's Charter also sought to improve access by ensuring that certain kinds of information on services were made available, and by setting standards that limited the maximum length of time that patients should wait for appointments at outpatients departments in hospitals or admission as an inpatient. All these considerations are important to patients and all the evidence confirms this. It seems clear that the Charter's efforts to improve access have not been wholly successful.

The main criticisms of the Patient's Charter regarding access to services can be summarised as:

- access is too narrowly defined
- insufficient focus on primary care
- access is particularly difficult for groups who experience social exclusion or discrimination in society.

A narrow definition of access

If a patient cannot get access to services when needed, it does not matter to that patient how good they are. Although the Patient's Charter broke new ground by guaranteeing admissions to hospital and setting down expectations about outpatient waiting times, the targets were modest. Since the length of waiting lists for hospital admissions was such a visible indicator of NHS performance and politically vulnerable, it was the aspect of access that received the greatest attention. As we have seen, the imperative to admit patients as they neared the 18-month ceiling did not necessarily reflect clinical need. For those who were very ill and possibly in pain, a delay of up to 18 months was unacceptable, and a maximum 12-month wait for coronary artery bypass grafts, introduced in April 1995, did little to change these concerns.

For outpatients, a maximum wait of 13 weeks (for 90 per cent of the population) or 26 weeks (for the remainder) still seemed too long, especially since the patient may have already waited a week or two to get an appointment with a GP, with a further delay while the referral letter was written. There was also concern about the way in which waiting lists are compiled and presented, with reports of informal waiting lists to get onto waiting lists, so that the published figures conceal the full extent of the problem.

For cancelled operations, the Patient's Charter standard was very modest:

> *Your operation should not be cancelled on the day you are due to go into hospital or after you have gone in. If it is you can expect to be admitted again within one month of the cancellation.*

It was not, clearly, a violation of charter standards to cancel operations two days before admissions, and it is therefore impossible to quantify the scale of the problem of those cancellations. Even with this limited ambition, however, the standards were breached on many occasions as the NHS Performance Guides (commonly known as league tables) demonstrate.

To summarise, there is much to be achieved even on the fairly limited aspects of access that are within the scope of the Patient's Charter.

Access for vulnerable people

Access to services is particularly difficult for the most vulnerable people in society, especially those with communication difficulties or disability, or who suffer from attitudes which exacerbate social exclusion. The interviews with vulnerable groups concerned with disability, homelessness, race and ethnicity, and the written material, confirmed the need for a much wider view of the problems of access to NHS services.

The Patient's Charter, it was said, fails to address access for homeless people where waiting lists for admission to hospital and delays of several months for outpatients are simply irrelevant. And even when homeless people are able to comply with the structures of the systems, they sometimes find that their access to services is limited by a lack of understanding and sympathy from staff.

Attitudes and awareness of specific needs, such as particular media for communication, are important aspects of access for other people too. The Director of the Greater London Association of Disabled People identified an awareness problem in the NHS which limits access of disabled people to appropriate services.

> *Sometimes disabled people are admitted to hospital for a particular complaint, but as their needs are not considered as a whole, they come out less mobile*

than when they went in. Their needs in terms of their disability and in terms of other aspects of their health care and their individuality need to be recognised.

Inadequate awareness of the needs of blind and deaf people were reported by the Royal National Institute for the Blind (RNIB) and the Royal National Institute for the Deaf (RNID).

The multi-ethnic women's health project in East London described racism and both direct and indirect discrimination in the NHS against people from minority ethnic groups which severely limited access to services. This could be a matter of attitude or actual practice within the NHS. Attempts to deal with such problems through improved cultural awareness were felt to be inadequate.

Tools for access

The NHS has to progress further by addressing the obstacles to access for those people who most need health care. Access cannot be guaranteed by word alone or by setting maximum waiting times. The following 'tools' need further development and support if any future charter is to improve access for everyone.

Information and communication

Information to patients and potential patients and their carers is a basic tool for enabling people to gain access to NHS services. In fact, this is too simple a concept and should be seen within the wider frame of effective communication in which patients are active partners, rather than passive recipients of information. The provision of information is discussed fully on pages 16–19.

Advocacy

There is a tradition in the NHS of using advocates to assist people in making their views heard, in helping them get the best from services on offer, and in helping services appreciate the needs of vulnerable people. Advocacy has greatly benefited work with minority ethnic groups, people with physical and sensory disabilities, people with learning disabilities and those with mental health problems. Support for independent advocacy is essential in enabling and empowering full use of documents such as charters and without access to advocacy, other access is likely to be a pious hope. However, advocacy projects have often been funded through time limited or 'soft' money, and many successful schemes are insecure.

Translation and interpretation

In spite of considerable effort, translation and interpretation in the NHS remain under-developed. This also applies to signing for deaf people. Interviews with vulnerable groups highlighted difficulties of access to primary care caused by lack of interpreters, or an unwillingness to use what was available and since the part played by primary care is increasing, failure to address this problem will further restrict access to health care for a growing number of people.

Increased awareness

Awareness of cultural factors, disability or social circumstances is a necessary but not complete part of improving access. Training can help in some instances but it can also reinforce prejudices. Secondments, shadowing of key personnel and opportunities for hands-on learning may here be necessary adjuncts to training.

Clarification of rights of access

A new look at the Patient's Charter is an opportunity to make explicit statements about rights of access to the NHS for all people and may indicate a need to clarify the difficulties faced by disabled people, refugees, asylum seekers and people from minority ethnic groups. It also suggests that those who commission and provide services should be clear about how they address access issues for people from all ethnic backgrounds and people with all kinds of disabilities.

Developing partnerships with patients

Rights and responsibilities

There is much support for a charter that protects the rights and responsibilities of those who work for the NHS as well as those who use it. However, some patients, according to our focus groups, felt that a charter should restrict itself to setting out rights, but most patients said that they would be happy to take account of their own responsibility to the NHS. They suggested four basic ways in which patients can meet their responsibilities to the NHS:

- make appropriate use of services
- behave in a civil way to staff
- try to co-operate in their own health care
- fund the service through taxation.

There are clearly two distinct views of Charter responsibilities. One, expressed by over-worked staff, is that patients should be reminded of their responsibilities to make them behave reasonably and encourage realistic expectations of what the NHS can offer. The other view (Bynoe 1996) is echoed by many patients' groups who see *responsibility* as a foundation of citizenship, participation and co-operation, and as a means of securing improved services and a responsible use of those services by informed citizens.

What can patients do?

Many of the comments from patients and their organisations showed considerable understanding of the ways in which they could be responsible:

- behave courteously and understand staff pressures
- take responsibility for self-care when appropriate and when given adequate information
- take part in qualitative feedback – seeing oneself in partnership with professionals
- maintain healthy lifestyles with assistance and support
- consider carefully information that is given
- provide material information about oneself and one's condition.

Several interviewees, however, emphasised that most patients already behave in a responsible way, and that only a minority fail to understand pressures on those who work in the NHS. Patients with long-term medical conditions and disabilities pointed out that they *were* responsible partners in their own care, and welcomed further opportunities to work with professionals.

While accepting the need to encourage and support patients' responsible behaviour, interviewees pointed out that there are problems which prevent some of them from behaving perfectly. To take an extreme example, some refugees and asylum seekers have been victims of torture, and even simple requests for information may be daunting for them.

A spokesperson for Crisis pointed out:

> *It would be easy to say that homeless people should turn up for appointments on time and not be drunk or violent, but how easy is it to be responsible for yourself when your life is out of control? When people are vulnerable, it is*

necessary to facilitate responsibility (e.g. helping them to keep appointments, getting them advocates). It is necessary to understand why people behave 'irresponsibly'.

What the NHS can do to support patients

The majority of patients are generally responsible and courteous and well aware of the pressures on services. Much can be done to support and reinforce patients who wish to use services wisely and well.

Honesty about services

The NHS must be honest about what can be provided. Raising expectations unrealistically leads to frustration, which in turn may provoke rudeness or worse. An honest approach must extend to the nature, quality and availability of services, and to the scope of what the NHS can and cannot do. This approach requires a much larger investment in raising fundamental issues such as rationing and prioritisation with the public.

Staff attitudes

NHS staff need to have positive attitudes to patients to encourage them to take responsibility for themselves. While most staff are sensitive and understanding, there is still evidence of staff behaviour that makes offensive assumptions about how certain types of patient are likely to behave.

Education and information for patients

Patients need to be told what is expected of them: for example, how to cancel appointments and how to use services appropriately.

Effective systems

An effective system is required to encourage responsible behaviour on the part of patients; for example, special phone numbers for patients to ring if they wish to change appointments, workable schedules for clinics, and staff trained to understand communication difficulties should all be considered.

Evidence suggests that efforts by patients to use the NHS wisely are sometimes frustrated by poor systems within the NHS itself and this was confirmed by our research. Almost three-quarters of providers and one-third of non-providers identified problems with NHS systems that contributed to difficulties with their responsibilities.

Towards real partnerships

Taken to extremes, the debate about rights and responsibilities can become sterile and rather naive. In reality, most patients wish to be helpful and co-operative while getting the best from the NHS and most staff try to offer a good service within the constraints of available resources. A culture of blame that suggests all would be well if everyone *else* behaved properly leads nowhere. What is required – and what is achievable – is a genuine progression towards partnership in the NHS, that values the integrity and goodwill of those who use services and also those who work inside it.

What should a new charter do?

The context of the new Patient's Charter is very different from the last one. We have a new government committed to a stakeholder society and there are new policy documents:

- the White Paper, *The New NHS: Modern – Dependable*, 1997
- a Green Paper, *Our Healthier Nation: A Contract for Health*, 1998
- and a new consultative document about performance standards *The New NHS: Modern and Dependable: A National Framework for Assessing Performance*, 1998.

The all describe the context within which the new charter will exist which emphasises health care at home, in the community, and in hospital, with primary care providing the main forum for health care for most people. It is a context in which partnerships between patients, carers, professionals, voluntary organisations and other statutory organisations are seen as essential ingredients of providing health care. This is a context where people take responsibility for their own health and behaviour where possible and where they will be taken care of by services when they cannot.

A clear purpose

This report shows the confusion felt by staff and patients about the aims of the Patient's Charter and how this increased pressure on staff and produced uncertainty among patients. A new charter should first of all be open and honest about its purpose. It should define clearly what its aims are and admit openly when extra money is needed to improve standards. Improving quality does not always cost money but there are times when it helps.

Charter development

A second important consideration is the way in which a new charter is developed. Any charter imposed from the top which does not include the wisdom of staff and patients will produce even more dissatisfaction than the first one. All our research emphasised the importance of involving users, carers, and staff in the process of drawing up a new national charter and in the development of local charters.

Equal attention to primary and community care services

The early version of the Patient's Charter came under fire for its concentration on acute, hospital services. People were still voicing these complaints in 1997 despite the fact that additional charters had, to some extent, corrected this bias. With the shift in policy towards primary care during since 1994 and the fact that primary and community care are where the majority of people experience health care, any new charter must redress that former imbalance.

The content of the Charter

Managers, clinicians and patients mentioned many topics which they wishes to see included in a new charter. Organisations submitting written evidence listed their priorities of quality standards for inclusion. Top of the list was standards for clinical effectiveness, followed by standards for effective information and communication. Then came: access to services; standards for primary and community care; standards which covered the quality of the patient experience including privacy, dignity and respect; standards for staff qualifications and attitudes. They also wished to see more focus on vulnerable groups and on partnerships with patients.

Patients in the focus groups produced a similar list which emphasised equity in access to and quality of services: clear information, positive interaction with staff, good quality clinical treatment, assurance of privacy and confidentiality and more choice in terms of registration with a GP and consultant referral. The fact that these rankings are so similar confirms the desirability of including them.

The ethos of a new charter

NHS staff and clinicians in our research were particularly keen for patients' responsibilities to be part of a new charter and patients, themselves, and their organisations supported this idea, though with reservations. It will be important not to appear to blame patients in any way. Most are aware that staff are often under pressure and that resources are limited. Many people are so afraid to 'bother doctors' that they wait until it is sometimes too late.

It is also clear that certain services are not user friendly. In clinics where 'failure to attend' rates have been audited and remedial action taken, problems have been resolved with little difficulty. Where staff complain that patients do not turn up for appointments and do not inform them, action can be taken to make it easier for patients to get in touch; patients are not incorrigibly inconsiderate. Equally important is the removal of what NHS staff called the 'negative context' of the existing charter and its management. They felt they were often scapegoated by managers and patients when things went wrong or standards were not achieved, even though problems were related to resources or demand. They wanted the government to acknowledge publicly the strengths of the NHS and its staff, and for the Charter not to be used as a weapon against them.

Managing and implementing a new charter

Although the content and ethos of a new charter are undoubtedly important, so too, are the processes by which it is introduced and implemented. Still suffering from the poor introduction of the current charter, staff made several suggestions for improving it:

- make allowances for the transition to the new charter by allowing time to implement it
- give better guidance on how to deal with overlapping and inconsistent standards
- encourage an environment where staff can be less defensive about complaints
- involve staff in the development of standards to ensure ownership and relevance.

Staff clearly found the monitoring of charter standards difficult and inappropriate and made useful suggestions here, too, for improving monitoring systems. They were:

- consider and improve the methods of monitoring standards
- improve the quality of data collected by integrating with other data collection systems
- use appropriate (e.g. qualitative) methods for standards which cannot be quantified, such as dignity and respect.

Conclusions and recommendations

Our research demonstrated considerable levels of agreement between patients and staff about the strengths and weaknesses of the Patient's Charter and the issues which a new charter should address.

An analysis of the priorities for inclusion in a new charter by staff (Chart D, Appendix 3 and Chart 6, Appendix 4) and patients (Chart 4, Appendix 4) identified eight key areas for discussion and development:

- clinical effectiveness/outcomes/need
- partnerships/involvement of patients and staff
- effective information and communication
- equity and access to service
- community and primary care services
- the quality of the patient experience
- staff training, qualification and attitude
- emphasis on vulnerable groups.

From this, our recommendations for a new Patient's Charter are grouped under the following headings:

- standards
- process
- infrastructure.

Standards

Given the strength of support for a Patient's Charter, a replacement should identify the values and principles to underpin all Patient's Charters and offer a model within which local standards can be set. Key standards should be discussed nationally and locally, and should cover:

- clinical need, effectiveness and outcomes
- the quality of the patient experience
- equity and access to services
- information and communication.

All these categories are covered in the draft national framework for assessing performance (NHS Executive 1998) and it would be sensible for charter standards to match those included in that framework where they are relevant.

Process

Partnerships

The development of the national and local charters should follow a process which includes staff, patients and carers, so that everyone feels an element of ownership in their local charter. This will help patients and staff to understand each other's perspectives and, hopefully, lay the groundwork for future partnerships in health care.

Vulnerable groups

Development should pay particular attention to vulnerable groups in the community, inviting them and their representatives to take part in the creation and monitoring of charters. Their main concern is achieving access to services and this needs special consideration.

Infrastructure

Resources

Although many features of a new charter can be achieved without financial resources, others will need money to be spent on them. The financial aspects should be considered during the development process and possible savings and expenditure identified. Each charter should make a definite statement about money available for it.

Monitoring

Implementation and management of a new charter will also need careful thought in relation to monitoring and feedback mechanisms.

Complaints should be dealt with positively and acted upon where necessary. Data from complaints analysis should be passed on to managers, clinicians and patients and ways of 'listening' to patient and carer experiences must be found. These should also be fed back to managers and clinicians.

Advocacy

Some form of advocacy service will be essential if the new Patient's Charter is to help vulnerable people gain access to the NHS. Such a service should be offered in every community and supported by language resources and outreach work.

This review of the Patient's Charter and the chance to rethink its aims and purpose have provided a welcome opportunity to involve patients and NHS staff in future developments. Although charters are only one way to improve the quality of patient care, they *can* make a difference to the patient experience. It should be remembered, however, that any charter can only achieve so much. Access to services and the quality of each patient's experience will be determined primarily by the principles, values and resources with which we all collectively endow our national health service.

References

Allen C (1995). Knowingly sold down the river. *Mental Health Nursing* 15(4):28.

Association of Community Health Councils (1996). *The Patients' Agenda*. London: ACHEW.

Audit Commission (1993). *What seems to be the matter?* London: Audit Commission.

Benton D (1993). Never mind the quality. *Nursing Standard* 7(40):50–1.

Berliner H (1997). You've been 'ad. *Health Service Journal* 11(9):27–8.

Bourgine P *et al*. (1984). La charte du malade. *Gestions – Hospitalieres*. Paris: Bliss.

Britten N, Shaw A (1997). Patients' experience of emergency admissions: how relevant is the British government's Patient's Charter? *Journal of Advanced Nursing* 19:1212–20.

Bruster B *et al*. (1994). National survey of hospital patients. *British Medical Journal* 309(96968):1542–6

Bynoe I (1996). *Beyond the Citizen's Charter – new directions for social rights*. London: Institute for Public Policy Research.

Carr Hill R, Ng F (1992). A confusion of charters. *Health Service Journal* 5(11):24–6.

Cohen P (1994). Passing the buck. *Nursing Times* 90(13):28–30.

Department of Health (1997). *The New NHS: Modern – Dependable*. Cm 3807. London: HMSO.

Department of Health (1996). *The Patient's Charter and You*. London: HMSO.

Friend B (1995). Shallow standards. *Nursing Times* 91(28):14–15.

Griffiths R *et al*. (1983) Letter to the Secretary of State, Norman Fowler.

Hart M. (1996). Improving the quality of out-patient services in NHS hospitals – some policy considerations. *International Journal of Health Care Quality Assurance* 9 July:28–38.

Hogg C (1994). *Working with Users: beyond the Patient's Charter*. London: Health Rights.

LeTouze S (1996). *Patients' Views of Hospital Care*. Canterbury: Centre for Health Services Studies, University of Kent.

Lorentzon M *et al*. (1996). Listening to patients in the NHS: a selective review of literature on patients' views about out-patient services in British hospitals. *Journal of Nursing Management* 4(3):163–9.

MacAlister L (1994). *British Journal of Nursing* 3(13):647–8.

McIver S (1992). *Obtaining the Views of In-Patients and Users of Casualty Departments*. London: King's Fund.

McIver S (1996). Towards a smarter charter. *Health Director* 2:20.

McIver S, Martin G (1996). Unchartered territory. *Health Service Journal* 19 Sept:24–5.

McSweeney (1994). Health remedy or sick joke? *Nursing Standard* 8(42):20–1.

National Opinion Polls (1994). *Development of the Patient's Charter*. Report of the findings of a qualitative research study. (unpublished)

NHS Executive (1998). *Our Healthier Nation: A contract for health*. Consultation Paper. Cm 3852. London: HMSO.

Rigge M (1997). Dr Who? *Health Service Journal* 11 Sept:24–6.

Rivett G (1998). *From Cradle to Grave*. London: King's Fund.

Ryland RK (1996). The Patient's Charter: the UK experience. *Journal of Advanced Nursing* 23:1059–60.

Tailor H, Mayberry JF (1995). The Patient's Charter: a survey of hospital out-patient views of their rights and ability to exercise them. *Social Science and Medicine* 40(10):1433–4.

Thain J (1992). Every Citizen's Right. *Nursing Times* 92(34):41.

The Labour Party (1997). *New Labour because Britain deserves better*. p.21.

Tschudin V (ed.) (1997). *Ethics – The Patient's Charter*. Scutari Press.

Tugend A and Harris L. (1997). Patients' rights in Europe. *Eurohealth* 3(1):31–3.

Viewpoint Readers' Panel (1995). Protecting the patient or just playing politics? *Nursing Standard* 10(3):46–7.

Wilder G (1995). Unchartered territory – can failure to meet national and local Patient's Charter standards be challenged in the courts? *Health Service Journal* 18 May:12.

Appendix 1

Main themes from the literature review

Most of the literature on the Patient's Charter is from professional journals, most of which are not refereed in an academic sense, and tend to be journalistic. There has been an apparent dearth of serious academic interest in the Charter. But it is impossible to gauge whether this reflects the current nature of academic interests, funding sources or its relative newness.

Variety of views

Overall, the literature strikingly demonstrates two characteristics. First, diversity of views on the value, or otherwise, of the Patient's Charter; and second, a degree of ambivalence on its fundamental idea and the rights and standards it contains as well as the ways in which they are monitored.

Some of this ambivalence is noted in an editorial by R. K. Ryland (1996) in *The Journal of Advanced Nursing*:

> *It would appear that many people working in the NHS resent the way in which the government departments have imposed the new rights and standards across the UK. This is, perhaps, a curious view. First, some working in the NHS have complained in the past that the government has been too concerned with volume and not enough with quality. So as soon as the government becomes concerned with quality there is an argument about the way in which it is done.*

Ryland also notes that Opposition parties (in 1996) claimed that the NHS was breaking up, and demanded reassurance that 90 per cent of patients were assessed in A&E within five minutes. Ryland describes this as:

> *A curious mind set: damned if you do and damned if you don't.*

In a similar vein, on waiting lists, Ryland argues:

Who in their right mind could possibly argue against these kinds of standards when previously there were none at all and there was no frame of reference for patients to assess whether or not the waiting time was excessive or against the rules?

However, other people would consider Ryland's view naive and disingenuous because published views tend to be those of NHS staff rather than users. For example, in a Viewpoint Readers' Panel (1995) in the *Nursing Standard*, there is a largely negative or hostile view of the Patient's Charter. Concerns include:

- manipulation of statistics
- volume-related throughput targets presented as qualitative standards
- inadequate focus on patients' responsibilities
- wrong measures used to indicate quality
- inadequate resources.

However, positive views are also expressed, including:

- a real step towards a better service for patients
- a useful clarifying of standards.

Perhaps the most telling comment is one headed *Good as a patient, bad as a nurse*. Nurses feel the Charter is a 'bludgeon to beat staff when the real problem is resourcing', but patients find it a 'useful means of exerting pressure which gets a response'.

Sometimes, the hostility to the very idea of a patient's charter is expressed in strong terms. Writing in *Mental Health Nursing*, Cris Allen (Allen 1995) says that the latest Patient's Charter standards for mental health guarantee nothing except more pressure on services and more disappointment and frustration for users. Allen also feels that achieving the standards would require 'a miracle', and fears that while raising expectations may be good, unrealistic charter standards 'merely raise hope'. But it is unclear whether Allen's doubts are pragmatic or principled for the author states that:

Healing and therapeutic relationships cannot be charterised.

Cynicism

Cynicism is a constant theme in the literature. We can explore this under several sub-headings:

- public attitudes
- political taint
- concerns about veracity of statistics
- lack of independent monitoring.

Public attitudes

There is interesting information from a study carried out by NOP Consumer Market Research (NOP 1994) for the Central Office of Information (COI) and the Department of Health. Prior to releasing the revised Patient's Charter in 1996, the COI on behalf of the Department of Health commissioned a research study to ensure that the views of the public were taken into account when its details were finalised. The study sought to explore a number of issues, including current awareness of the Charter, the ability to understand the purpose and scope of the Patient's Charter leaflet, reactions to design, format and comprehensibility, what people wished to see included in it and opinions of the new standards that ministers had already decided it should contain.

The following points emerged about attitudes to the Patient's Charter:

- there was low awareness and little interest in it
- it was seen as telling patients what they could reasonably expect from NHS services – entitlement to services was felt to be the main issue
- dissatisfaction with politics and politicians had a negative effect on the Charter, especially when it was linked with central government.

There is also interesting information from a survey of general hospital outpatients on their rights and their ability to exercise them (Tailor & Mayberry 1995). This shows that the codification of patients' rights in a charter has begun to have significant effects on the day-to-day running of hospitals in Britain, which includes patients pointing to failures in the standard of service. However, this depends on awareness by the community and on a belief that these rights can be exercised successfully.

Tailor & Mayberry investigated the views of patients on the contents of the Charter and whether they believed they could make use of it. Ninety-eight per cent knew of their right to be registered with a GP, and 95 per cent were aware of the right to receive emergency care at any time. But only 42 per cent knew of the right to receive detailed information on local health services, and 44 per cent knew they could have any complaint about the NHS investigated. There was also in all instances a considerable gap between the percentage of patients who were aware of a particular right and the percentage who believed they were allowed to exercise that right. For example, although 80 per cent of patients knew of their right to be referred to a consultant acceptable to them, only 64 per cent thought they could exercise this right.

Political taint

The point about political taint in the Charter is made by several sources. NOP reports:

> *The more publication was seen as emanating from central government the more its purpose was believed to be political and the less credible its message.* (NOP 1994)

Phil McSweeney (1994) sees the NHS reforms as a two-pronged attack, the first seeking to raise quality of care and cost efficiency through internal competition, and the second empowering consumers by raising their expectations. The author also mentions that nurses could be 'caught in the crossfire' between managing patients' expectations without knowing what had been purchased. McSweeney recognises that there appear to be gains, such as improvements in waiting times for admission and in outpatients, the growth of immediate assessment in A&E and standards for re-admission following cancellation of admission. However, it is unclear exactly where the cause of such improvements lies. The author lists a range of ways in which performance is reviewed, quite apart from the Patient's Charter and concludes that poor reception of the Charter is due to:

> *Being unable to divorce it from its political context, it is a major top-down imposed management project . . . the Patient's Charter, though stopping short of taking away nurses' will to live, has robbed them of ownership of their quality initiatives.*

A similar point is also made by Phil Cohen (1994) who states that nurses have made little contribution to charter policy, which has largely been imposed on them.

Concerns about the veracity of statistics

Concerns about the reliability of Patient's Charter figures are made in the strongest possible terms. Friend (1995) claims that pressure to meet Charter standards means that some hospitals are fiddling the figures:

> *In the worst account of charter cheating, patients were said to have been transferred from trolleys to chairs to comply with A&E waiting time limits.*

Friend also claims that hospitals offer appointments only when they know they can meet the relevant targets. She also notes that the Department of Health denies hard evidence of any problems, that the Audit Commission inspects the data collection system to ensure that information is accurate and that chief executives personally have to sign off the data.

However, given pressures on them, it would be surprising if some staff did not feel justified in fiddling the figures, and Friend also reports that a Royal College of Nursing adviser has been contacted by nurses threatened with disciplinary action if they do not meet Patient's Charter targets.

There is also concern in the literature about whether measured improvements are genuine. This is not just a comment on whether figures are to be believed, but on whether they throw adequate light on complex problems. Or, as Hart puts it:

> *Quantitative indicators are nearly always seized upon because they measure that which is measurable, rather than that which is significant. (Hart 1996)*

MacAlister (1994) also suggests that crude data may mislead. For example, improvements in the waiting times for certain treatments may increase writing times for others. Carr Hill & Ng (1992) also doubt the reliability of monitoring data. They conclude that the NHS Executive seems ignorant of how hospitals work and of the complexity of monitoring data. They also suggest that Performance Related Pay generates the potential for anomalies in the reporting of data. Staff polls such as the one previously referred to (Viewpoint Readers Panel 1995) also show a high level of disbelief of 'official' figures.

Lack of independent monitoring

Worries about the figures are not eased by the lack of real independent monitoring of the data that is collected. McIver & Martin (1996) point out that there is little research into whether rights are being upheld. They say that the NHS Executive does not monitor or investigate compliance with the rights in the same way that it does other standards.

This is a fundamental issue for some commentators. The Association of Community Health Councils for England and Wales argues for a strengthened rights-based Charter, backed by more effective enforcement:

> *In proposing new or stronger rights the question obviously arises as to how we think such rights should be enforced. We do not consider that patients should have to resort to law in order to obtain them. Instead we suggest that the monitoring and assurance of all charter rights demands a more effective machinery than that which is currently available to patients.* (ACHCEW 1996)

ACHCEW proposes creation of an independent Health Rights Commission for this purpose.

Status of the Patient's Charter

Enforceable rights?

Confusion about the exact nature and status of the Patient's Charter crops up several times in the literature. The extent to which Patient's Charter rights and standards can be enforced, if at all, is unclear and there is uncertainty as to whether it is actually concerned with real rights or is just a wish-list.

Hogg distinguishes between different kinds of charters:

> *A Charter is a statement of fundamental principles, which may incorporate rights and standards. There is a distinction between charters produced for people and charters or declarations of rights produced by people themselves.* (Hogg 1994)

She states that rights in health care are 'largely symbolic', and few rights in health care meet the criteria normally used for rights; that is, they are not inalienable or enforceable in law. Hogg sees the Patient's Charter as more of a consumer's charter than a citizen's charter to empower patients.

The issue of how far legal redress might be used is further explored by Wilder (1995). Wilder notes that some Patient's Charter rights, (such as that of access in certain circumstances to one's own medical records, or the right to have any proposed treatment, its risks and alternatives explained) are already statutory or common law rights. But what about other Patient's Charter standards, such as maximum waiting times for admission of 18 months, or a maximum wait of

26 weeks for an outpatient appointment? Wilder asks whether a failure to comply with the Patient's Charter amounts to a breach of statutory duty to provide an adequate health service. Court cases in the 1980s where patients sued the Secretary of State along with regional and area health authorities failed as the NHS Act 1977 gives clear discretion on how financial resources are to be used. However, Wilder asks whether promises in the Patient's Charter indicate that the Secretary of State for Health has already determined how at least some of the available resources are to be spent. Is a health service body acting reasonably if the result of its decision is a failure to achieve a standard which the Secretary of State has said all patients are entitled to receive? These questions have not yet been answered by the courts.

Several writers claim that the Charter does not safeguard rights. Thain argued in 1992 that a Bill of Rights and not a patient's charter is urgently needed to protect elderly patients from the uncertainties of a market-driven NHS:

> *In creating a patient's charter the government is shirking responsibility for many of the problems patients are experiencing as a result of changes in the health service*. (Thain 1992)

A firmer basis in social rights is also strongly supported by Bynoe (1996), who is critical of many aspects of the Citizen's Charter, and its offshoots such as the Patient's Charter, but he also acknowledges that both have strengths that merit further development. For example by:

- improving the information given to those seeking or using services
- measuring differences between comparable services to reveal the inequities between them and helping locate the causes
- the Charter Mark award scheme
- reforms to complaints and redress systems
- lay involvement in inspection and complaints adjudication.

On behalf of The Institute of Public Policy Research, Bynoe goes on to propose a programme based on the following six principles:

- *fair treatment* – to guarantee fair treatment to those seeking or using public services
- *entitlement* – to meet the public's informed expectations of entitlement
- *participation* – to ensure that services are responsive to users and to encourage greater public involvement in planning services and holding them accountable

- *openness* – to render public services more open in their dealings with users and the public
- *accountability* – to improve public accountability by making audit and inspection more effective
- *co-operation* – to stress to citizens and users their respective responsibilities and the value of a co-operative approach.

Each of these principles is supported by a proposal for action.

The blurring of rights and standards in the current Patient's Charter has also been noted as a source of confusion. Carr Hill & Ng (1992) looked in 1992 at local charters in 140 health authorities and 50 family health service authorities. They noted that in many of them, 'rights' were included under 'standards' and vice versa, sometimes with justification. However, definition of a right was not so clear: for example, the 'right' to be attended to within a certain period of time at an outpatient clinic is dependent on resources available at that time and is therefore not a rights-based entitlement.

Carr Hill & Ng comment:

> *Pronouncing 'rights' and 'standards' without agreement on the desired outcomes and without, apparently, understanding the processes by which their attainment can be monitored flies in the face of the little we have all learned from the quality assurance movement over the last decade.*

Local and national charters

The confusion between local and national charter standards was also examined by Carr Hill & Ng, who found that only 30 per cent of those they examined separated national from local standards. Moreover, few staff knew how the local Charter differed from the national, or even where it was posted in their unit.

However, local charters are seen to possess a number of positive attributes by McIver (1996), who notes that commissioners and providers are encouraged to develop local charters and asks whether these will duplicate the national Charter or will address different issues. Her conclusion is that local charters can build on the clear set of standards because they are able to address local concerns and be monitored locally. Local charters can also provide the detail necessary to cover aspects that are important to specific groups of users, such as children, elderly people and minority groups, and to those using a particular service, for example, mental health service users. McIver notes:

> *The key to producing local charters is to develop them with service users, so that standards relate to aspects of the service they consider important.*

Quality or quantity?

Much of the literature is concerned with the thorny issue of whether the Patient's Charter has had a positive, negative or neutral effect on the quality of health services. We have already noted concerns that quantitative information is sought and more highly valued than perhaps more significant qualitative data (Hart 1996). Benton observes that little advice was given on qualitative methods in the Technical Guidance for the Patient's Charter issued in 1992 (Benton 1993). He also notes that most of the measures applied in the Patient's Charter are either process or output oriented, and not outcome oriented. Benton's concerns about quality also stems from possible conflicts between individuals and purchasers. He states that the Patient's Charter is focused on the rights of individuals, whereas the purchasing authority focuses ultimately on local population requirements. To achieve value for money, purchasers may place larger (and therefore fewer) contracts, which limit individual choices. He says that commissioners should pay attention to quality.

An editorial in the *British Journal of Nursing* (MacAlister 1994) questions the value of NHS league tables. Since 1974, star ratings have been given for performance on various criteria drawn from the Patient's Charter, such as the percentage of patients seen within 30 minutes of their appointment time, the percentage of those assessed within five minutes of arrival in A&E, the numbers who fail to be readmitted following cancellation on the day of an operation, the percentage of people treated as day cases for specified conditions, and waiting times for admission for inpatient treatment for specified surgical conditions. However, the league tables have nothing to say about the quality of clinical care that is provided by hospitals. As MacAlister comments:

> *This being so, it is easy to envisage a situation where hospitals providing the highest standards in clinical care may be unfairly discriminated against by purchasers on the basis of their lesser position in the league tables. Surely, if there is any case at all for distinguishing between hospitals in this manner, it is important to ensure that the criteria used are related to worthwhile measures of quality.*

MacAlister and others warn that it is important to make an accurate interpretation of the performance ratings as data do not always speak clearly for themselves. For example, patients may be assessed at A&E within five minutes, but may then wait several hours for treatment. In addition, crude data may mislead, and improvements in waiting times for some treatments may simply increase waiting times for others.

Further comments on quality and waiting times are made by Lorentzon *et al.* (1996). Lorentzon and colleagues conducted a review of literature on patients' views about outpatient services, with special emphasis on the role of nurses. They discovered a central emphasis on factors that were easily measurable, such as waiting times in outpatient departments, but a comparative neglect of more qualitative aspects, which are likely to be of greater importance to patients. They point out that, from the patients' point of view, long waits in outpatients departments may not be the most important aspect of the outpatient experience. Also, waiting times were not measured as a rule in relation to the severity of the patient's clinical condition. Long waits may be more acceptable for patients who attend with routine, non-acute conditions than they are for seriously ill patients.

Lorentzon notes that in addition to waiting times, patients were concerned about staff attitudes, physical comforts and transport to and from outpatients departments. In other words, the main focus was on

> *The doctor-patient encounter and on conditions which would make this easier.*

Another concern about the quality vs quantity debate occurs with regard to two-year waits for admission (Cohen 1994). Although the reduction in two-year waits was said to apply universally, many CHCs observed that shorter waits were adversely affected, and there were cases of priority being given to patients with less clinical need than others. This raises fundamental questions on the nature and quality of patient care, and the underlying policy for seeing and treating patients.

Friend asserts bluntly that the quality of care is being sacrificed to attain star ratings and she asks whether the scramble to meet targets is pushing out good quality patient care in favour of a '*have-a-nice-day culture*'. (Friend 1995)

Quality and what users want

An improvement which can be measured easily may not go far enough to meet the aspirations for improved service quality. LeTouze (1997) reports on a study by McIver (1992) in which the key issues for users are:

- information and communication
- treatment and care (including outcome)
- staff friendliness and competence
- the efficiency of procedures including admission and discharge
- ward environment and facilities.

Information and communication are particularly important to users, as the Audit Commission confirms (Audit Commission 1993). This report identified poor communication as the primary source of dissatisfaction with health care, and found that common complaints included:

- not enough information
- information not clear
- information not what the patient wants
- information given too late
- information given too hurriedly.

However, there are indications (Bruster *et al.* 1994 and LeTouze 1996) that in spite of the Patient's Charter stipulating certain (albeit limited) rights to information, for example, on proposed treatments, risks and alternatives, such information is not always provided adequately. (See section on 'Information', below)

There has also been comment in the literature on quality issues in A&E (Britten & Shaw 1994). This study evaluates the Patient's Charter from the perspective of patients admitted via the A&E department and uses qualitative data about the concerns of these patients to judge whether the standards set out in the Charter match their priorities and, conversely, if there are issues of importance to these patients which it ignores. They conclude that the rights and standards in the Charter are generally appropriate to these patients' experience, but that definitions may be too narrow. Important issues of quality that are not given appropriate attention in the Patient's Charter are:

- *pain relief* – not always timely or adequate
- *giving information* – patients sometimes perceived requests for information

as irrelevant or repetitive
- *receiving information* – poor information on waiting times and long periods of not knowing what was happening
- *reception staff* – concerns about receptionists' interpersonal skills
- *examinations and investigations* – sometimes painful and humiliating
- *physical environment* – problems with smoking and non-smoking areas, car parking, telephones, ventilation, smells, lack of pillows and opening times of the pharmacy
- *other people in casualty* – numbers and conduct of other people, and need for a visible security presence in A&E.

Britten & Shaw (Britten & Shaw 1994) state that:

> *The patient wants rather more than the recent British government documents suggest.*

Hogg (1994) also indicates that users' charters (as opposed to government charters) are concerned about a number of quality issues that are not central to the current Patient's Charter, including:

- the boundary between home and hospital and health and social care, where present charters concentrate on acute hospital care
- other services that affect their ability to cope with their illness, such as income, housing and child care
- access to services where using them may lead to discrimination and even loss of civil rights
- the way the service is provided and whether their autonomy is respected
- defining in detail what is meant by the general expressions of goodwill in the Charter.

User involvement

There are indications in the literature (Hogg 1994, McIver 1996) that user involvement and the development of partnerships are of central importance. Hogg states:

> *The process by which they [charters] are developed and monitored is more important than the words that make up the Charter. Involving users in planning and evaluating services requires commitment, expertise, patience and resources. There is a need for a national framework within which local*

charters can be developed and monitored. It is as much on the process as the actual standards that the national framework needs to focus.

Information

This section revisits concerns about information to examine the nature of the information that is needed and given, and whether it is in accordance with the requirements of the Patient's Charter. Rigge (1997) asks a fundamental question. She takes as an example the right of a patient to be referred to a consultant acceptable to them, but asks how can any patient know about consultants, since:

There is no acceptable way to get reliable up-to-date information about centres of excellence, or within their specialty, about consultants who specialise.

She notes that this is a problem even for GPs, who may have to make referrals to a specialist whom they have not explicitly selected since they have no information on which to base their choice. Rigge notes that the NHS Code of Practice on Openness suggests that information about a consultant's training, qualifications and special interests should be made available on request. However, a telephone survey of every acute trust in one NHS region revealed that half of them provided no information at all on their consultants either to GPs or patients.

Some of the difficulties of collecting and disseminating such information are related by Berliner, drawing on the American experience, who predicts use of the Internet for providing details about doctors and hospitals, but warns of the lack of regulation or quality control of Internet sites. (Berliner 1997)

Responsibilities

Rights and responsibilities are closely linked. Some of the literature suggests the Patient's Charter has enhanced patients' rights without encouraging a corresponding growth in their responsibilities. The Editor's note to Cohen (1994) raises the problem of increased complaints:

The Patient's Charter, many health professionals would agree, has been more trouble than it is worth and does little to ensure consumers of health services get a better deal. Indeed, many feel it has done little more than raise clients' expectations and encourage them to complain. As one GP sees it, it is 'merely

> *another excuse for the chattering classes to put pressure on nurses and doctors who are already stretched to the limit'*.

This opens a debate about responsibility that prefers to damp down patients' expectations and complaints and contrasts with Bynoe (1996), whose concept of such responsibility is rooted in good citizenship, participation and co-operation, which leads to improved services and a responsible use of them by well-informed citizens.

The Association of Community Health Councils for England and Wales deals with the issue briefly:

> *It is accepted that patients also have certain responsibilities, for example, to let health service staff know if an appointment cannot be kept, to inform the surgery of a change of address or to return equipment when it is no longer needed.* (ACHCEW 1996)

It seems that although there is considerable interest, in developing responsibilities, particularly from certain staff groups, not much has been published to suggest how this could be done. Some of the articles on patients' needs and views (Rigge 1997, Hogg 1994) address the issue of responsibilities by implication, but seldom tackle the challenge directly.

Appendix 2

Interviews with voluntary organisations, patients' organisations and representatives of vulnerable groups

Face to face interviews were conducted with the following organisations:

- College of Health (Marianne Rigge)
- Carers National Association (Francine Bates)
- Association of Community Health Councils for England and Wales (Toby Harris and ACHCEW Information Team)
- Age Concern England (Jane Whelan)
- National Consumer Council (Barbara Meredith, Mike Bartram and Anita Abell)
- Patients Association (Cathy Gritzner)
- MIND (Judi Clements)
- Long-term Medical Conditions Alliance (Judy Wilson and meeting of LMCA member organisations).

Although many of the themes in the literature review are echoed again here, it is important to locate ideas and opinions in their context. Many of the issues summarised here were expressed in similar terms by different organisations and individuals and it would be tedious to attribute sources in each case, but an exception has been made where there were differences of opinion on a particular issue, or where the source of a view is particularly relevant.

Is a patient's charter important?

There were varied opinions about this. It is certainly an important issue, but not one which patients and service users regard as one of their most important concerns. The Patient's Charter was still seen by some people as John Major's big idea, and closely associated with the last government. It was, therefore, still viewed with suspicion. However, several organisations took an active interest in rights and standards covered by it, even if they did not locate their concerns within its framework.

The College of Health made the point that although charters and helplines are often denigrated as middle-class fancies, that was not their experience as many 'ordinary people' used the helplines and were concerned about rights, including information and access to treatment. Other organisations, such as Age Concern England, felt that less than one-quarter of 1 per cent of their respondents had used the Patient's Charter effectively, and these were articulate people. The point was also made that there is such widespread confusion about how the NHS is run that the chance of being able to invoke rights in a system that is not comprehensible are remote.

There was widespread feeling that any review of the Patient's Charter would have little effect, as many of its limitations were likely to continue, despite the change of government. Even so, most voluntary organisations wanted an opportunity to influence changes if possible.

ACHCEW said that the Patient's Charter had at least put rights and standards on the agenda. It had also raised expectations, not because people now knew what their specific rights were, but because the Charter changes the culture, and patients assume that they must have some sort of right to a decent service.

No teeth?

Most organisations believed that the Patient's Charter had 'no teeth'. Even where rights and standards were appropriate (and there was disagreement on this), the chances of using the Charter to enforce them was seen as remote. ACHCEW has developed clear ideas on enforcement with their proposals for an independent Health Rights Commission.

Several organisations felt it would help to be more explicit about what could be expected from the Patient's Charter. What sanctions might be imposed on services that failed to meet the Charter requirements and how would such sanctions work in hospitals, for instance.

Advocacy

The enforcement and implementation of rights was linked by several voluntary organisations to the need for better access to independent advocacy.

MIND made this point particularly strongly, noting that to be effective services need adequate resources.

Too much stress on acute services

The Patient's Charter was felt to be too oriented towards acute services. Many voluntary organisations work for people with long-term conditions and for those who are regular users of primary care and community services (both health and social care) such as older people and people with mental health problems. They wanted to make the Charter more relevant to their needs.

Second opinions

The limited right to a second opinion in contentious case was seen to need revision; that is, limited by the need for the GP's agreement, by lack of knowledge of appropriate specialists and also by the difficulty of a recommended provider not having a contract with the purchaser. Many voluntary organisations would welcome the unconditional right to a second opinion, including access to a second opinion in primary care, without having to change their GP. MIND's enthusiasm for second opinions was qualified by research that draws on reports of the Mental Health Act Commission which shows that second opinions nearly always agree with first opinions. They are also concerned about patients' rights to have alternatives explained to them and choices given to patients on their treatment options.

GP services

The desire to extend the Patient's Charter to include primary care was general rather than specific. But one specific point that cropped up regularly was that too many patients, especially older people, had difficulty registering or retaining their right to be registered, with a GP. The GPs' right to remove patients from their lists without giving reasons was seen as unfair and outdated.

Quality issues

Patients' organisations were concerned that the Charter had mainly been preoccupied with quantity and throughput. The quality issues that were of deep concern included:

- patients feel they are hurried and out of control and this may later lead to litigation to resolve difficulties that arise as a result

- staff attitudes and rudeness need to be looked at
- staffing levels should be improved
- workers of the same sex as the patient and single-sex wards are needed (especially in mental health)
- better attention should be paid to feeding patients in hospital
- access to bathing and showering at home is needed for older people
- quality of information to patients needs to be improved (see also section on 'Information').

However, patients' organisations did not necessarily feel a charter was the best vehicle for improving these quality issues. Discussions indicate that these were the *kinds* of issues they wanted attention focused on, rather than diverting staff energy to things that mattered less to patients.

Carers

There was a diversity of views on how best to safeguard and promote carers' rights in the context of a charter. No-one doubted that carers have rights, but the perennial issue of how to balance a patient's need for confidentiality with a carer's need for information remained a problem, as did the question of how to resolve conflicts of interest between patients and carers. Potential conflicts are particularly sensitive in the field of mental health.

There was uncertainty on whether there should be a separate carer's charter, or whether carers' rights should be part of the Patient's Charter, or whether this would confuse the issues. However, the Carers National Association presented a strong and detailed argument for family and carer issues to be integrated more fully into the Patient's Charter. In particular, the Association advocates better information for carers, that would include information about statutory rights, and more rights across the health and social care divide. However, concerns about waiting times at hospital that did not feature on everyone's agenda, from a patient's perspective, *were* important to carers who had a tight schedule of caring duties to adhere to.

Information

For those groups that were interviewed information was the key issue. It was seen as the cornerstone of being able to exercise rights meaningfully and the existing Patient's Charter is regarded as very unambitious in this respect. The following information requirements were mentioned:

- information on medical condition, including diagnosis (mental health patients in particular may have years of treatment without a diagnosis)
- information on social and medical implications of diagnosis
- information about health services and other related services
- information about self-help groups and organisations
- information on clinicians (qualifications, training, success rates, outcomes, number of procedures performed)
- information on rights to services (especially non-medical alternatives for mental health patients)
- similar information from other sources that can be compared over time
- good infrastructure to help people gain access to information
- information on the NHS and how it works – greater accountability
- information on how the NHS gets and spends its money
- anonymised reports of audits
- clinical guidelines and clinical indicators
- information on who will be operating/carrying out a procedure on patient.

Consent

The right to informed consent is a right that needs to be strengthened. The need for high-quality information confirms this, but relatively simple rights, such as the right to a copy of the consent form, would be welcomed.

Measuring performance

Echoing the literature, there was grave doubt about the efficacy of measuring and monitoring Patient's Charter data so far. There was in particular strong agreement on the need to take a qualitative as well as a quantitative view, which could be stated simply as a need to listen to patients. Ways to accomplish this were mentioned, including:

- focus groups
- market research techniques
- on-going panels of regular users
- opportunistic surveys and discussions in waiting areas
- publishing of local qualitative studies
- inspections by outside independent body
- expanded CHC role
- flexibility about how the views of users are sought.

In addition, it was felt that more attention should be paid to needs that remain unmet, using information from members of the public. The role of GPs in providing feedback on services should also be recognised and better exploited.

Interface with non-NHS services

Voluntary organisations are very concerned that rights in the NHS are meaningless unless they are supported by other rights. The National Consumer Council (NCC), for example, pointed to the absence of a charter for residential care homes. MIND was concerned about the need for rights to a fair share of employment.

Complaints

Charter rights concerning complaints were felt to be inadequate. In particular, the new complaints system was seen as a failure in primary care, where the need for the patient to take their complaint to the practitioner to seek local resolution deterred most people.

The Patient's Charter was said to confer irrelevant rights: for example, the right to have a complaint investigated and eventually signed by the chief executive was irrelevant if nothing improved as a consequence. In any case, since most people unhappy with poor services do not complain, a concentration on formal complaints produced little excitement in the groups that were interviewed.

What kind of charter?

A great deal of work needs to be done here, for while there was no shortage of ideas on what is important to patients, there was a diversity of views on whether a patient's charter should be a long or a short document based around national and/or local charters. Views also diverged on whether or not disease-specific charters would be more useful, and whether the Patient's Charter should concentrate on rights to which there was a legal redress, or whether it should merely be a standard-setting document.

Responsibilities

Most people agreed that patients had responsibilities as well as rights, but those interviewed were uncertain how to give substance to these responsibilities. There was also concern that the impetus for stressing responsibilities came from managers and clinicians who wished to curb demands from patients. Some organisations had already conducted work on patients' responsibilities, such as ACHCEW, who have studied patients who do not attend hospital. Patients often try to behave responsibly but find that NHS systems make it difficult for them to do so. Others, especially patients with long-term conditions, felt they were always trying to take responsibility, and what was needed was a recognition of their right to be involved in discussions about self-management.

However, patients' responsibilities can be construed much more widely, and possible responsibilities mentioned included:

- behaving courteously and showing an understanding of staff pressures
- taking responsibility for self-care when appropriate and when given adequate information
- taking part in qualitative feedback – seeing oneself in partnership with professionals
- following a healthy lifestyle, with assistance and support and possibly with incentives to do so
- taking proper note of information that is given (but mental health patients especially would be wary of anything that suggested a responsibility on the patient to accept the prescribed treatment)
- providing information about oneself and one's condition.

It was also mentioned that patients need to understand what the NHS can and cannot do, and further public debate on NHS functions and rationing are needed.

The Patients' Association also suggested that the NHS had to be honest about situations where they could not help and divert patients to the voluntary sector who can sometimes deliver better care.

A further concern was that sanctions on patients who do not act responsibly should not exclude them from essential care. It was also felt that a right to treatment should not be conditional on lifestyle, and that an educational approach, rather than the heavy hand of sanctions, was the better way forward.

Interviews with representatives of vulnerable groups

We conducted interviews with organisations or groups we felt might have difficulties with access to the NHS or quality within the NHS.

We identified the following areas where interviews could be particularly enlightening:

- physical disability groups
- those with sensory disabilities (blind and deaf)
- minority ethnic groups
- refugees
- those affected by HIV and AIDS
- homeless people.

We interviewed people from each of the following groups:

- Greater London Association of Disabled People (GLAD)
- Royal National Institute for the Blind (RNIB)
- Royal National Institute for Deaf People (RNID)
- Multi-ethnic women's project
- Refugee Council
- London Lighthouse Service Users Consultative Forum (HIV/AIDS)
- Crisis (homelessness).

The interviews were conducted by telephone except for the multi-ethnic women's project, where we spoke to people at a meeting with a large group of health advocates. The material from these interviews is not intended to stand alone. The interviews gave us an in-depth understanding of issues that had also been explored in other parts of the research, but here we were able to focus more clearly on problems of discrimination, access to services or exclusion from services for people who may have had historical difficulties in getting the best from mainstream health services.

Main concerns from the interviews

Usefulness of the Patient's Charter

While other parts of the research suggest a wide range of opinion on the Patient's Charter, these groups took a dimmer view of it.

Some groups did have positive comments to make, at least about the principles that lay behind the Charter. The RNIB felt it had been important in setting down rights and expectations. They regarded it as a first step in producing standards that empowered blind and visually impaired people holistically and not just in relation to sight issues. The RNID and the Refugee Council also welcomed the Charter as a limited step in the right direction.

On the other hand, the multi-ethnic women's project variously described it as 'a waste of paper', 'window dressing', and 'worthless'. It was seen as a hypocritical 'cover-up' for lack of resources and cuts to spending on health. They said that what was achieved in local health services came from advocacy and not through the Patient's Charter. Nor was it seen by Crisis as having made much of a contribution for homeless people in the NHS, since it did not address the key issues of access for homeless people.

The Refugee Association and the London Lighthouse Service Users Consultative Forum pointed out, as did others, that the Patient's Charter might be more useful if more people knew of its existence and what it contained.

Several groups raised concerns about a lack of enforcement or implementation of rights and standards in the Charter and others criticised its omissions such as primary care services and professions allied to medicine such as physiotherapy, and the specialist community and rehabilitation services used by some of the groups.

Quality issues in the NHS

These very diverse groups, not surprisingly, prioritised a wide range of quality issues. A common theme, however, was that all patients need to be treated as individuals, and not stereotyped the way many of them had been within their groups. The importance of the awareness among staff of the issues and difficulties faced by particular sections of the community was universally acknowledged, though awareness training was never seen as a substitute for tackling prejudice.

Another theme echoed by several groups was the need for independent advocacy as a prerequisite to achieving access to quality in the NHS for those who were disadvantaged or suffered discrimination or prejudice. Health advocates of the multi-ethnic women's project said that there could be no quality without equality. For groups where prejudice and discrimination still blight their experience of the NHS, access to services was the most fundamental aspect of quality. As well as advocacy, interpreting of languages other than English, including signing, was seen as a cornerstone of access. Information in appropriate forms, such as large print for those with visual impairment and text telephones for those with hearing difficulties, was essential if the principles of a charter were to apply to everyone.

Groups had different suggestions for a new charter, though access and communication were mentioned most often as vitally important.

Information

Many groups were concerned that information given to them should be genuine information about what is really available. For example, it was pointed out that it is not helpful to tell homeless people that everyone has a right to register with a GP when, in practice, many cannot do so.

The multi-ethnic women's project had a long list of the kind of information required:

- letters from the hospital in community languages and in plain English on interpretation and advocacy
- information about GPs
- information on out-of-hours services
- information about rights
- information about what to do after discharge from hospital, and about after-care, available in translation if required)
- information on specific illnesses and conditions (oral and written information), especially when bad news is given
- information on how to complain
- politely worded information on how to cancel appointments.

The London Lighthouse Service Users Consultative Forum also added that they required information on developments in medical treatments, long-term outcomes and other matters specifically related to their medical conditions as they feared that long-term budget decisions are being taken on information from short-term research.

Each of the disability groups also stressed the need for information in appropriate formats.

National or local charters

Perhaps because these groups had suffered from a lack of equality within the NHS, they were all much in favour of national rather than local charters, though some felt there was a requirement for work at a local level to ensure that realistic standards were provided to match local need. Many said that the real question is how a charter is used. Crisis suggested that each locality could be asked to identify their three most vulnerable groups and to report on how they had applied the Charter to those groups.

Rights and responsibilities

All groups recognised the importance of rights and responsibilities for patients and welcomed the idea of increased partnership with NHS staff. It was said that NHS staff need to have positive attitudes to patients to encourage them to take responsibility for themselves.

Several approaches were identified to enable people to become responsible:

- advocacy (not just to enable people to use services)
- education of patients on their responsibilities
- effective NHS systems to enable people to behave responsibly
- greater involvement of service users
- better information to support self-management by patients.

However, it was pointed out that a uniform view of how patients should behave must take account of the realities of life for different groups of people. For example, one can demand that homeless people arrive for appointments on time, but how easy is it to be responsible for yourself when your life is out of control? We must understand why people behave 'irresponsibly'.

There are other, basic aspects of behaviour that need to be understood in context. For example, refugees, particularly those who have suffered torture, may appear uncooperative because they find it difficult to discuss their condition with staff, when that is not their intention.

The need for consultation

Although a review of the Patient's Charter was welcomed, the need for future standards to be the subject of genuine consultation was felt to be essential to its chances of success.

Appendix 3

The written evidence

This appendix summarises a survey of 182 organisations which included health authorities, acute trusts, acute and community trusts, community and mental health trusts, ambulance trusts, general practitioners, voluntary organisations, royal colleges, professional organisations and trade unions. Details of the methods used and response rates are contained in Appendix 5. The data in this report are based on 89 completed responses (i.e. 49 per cent of the total sample).

The existing Patient's Charter

A mixed blessing

The existing Patient's Charter has been useful in some limited ways. The overall impression from the replies to the questionnaire was that it had provided a starting point and a framework within which organisations had been able to tackle aspects of quality and service delivery. It was useful because it had provided a first definition of national principles and standards for the NHS. It had offered a focus for patient-oriented services and was felt to redress the imbalance caused by a hitherto professionally-oriented service. It had also highlighted specific issues such as waiting times. Some organisations had found it a useful device for introducing change and reviews of procedures and one respondent said it was:

> *A tool which had made some contribution to change …*

Another described it as:

> *An initial attempt at improving standards …*

Health authorities said that it had acted as a useful starting point for performance improvements and for the identification of problems with services and with internal procedures. It had also raised staff awareness of the need to make services more responsive to patients, particularly in relation to waiting times. Acute trusts and acute and community trusts expressed similar views. The response from the royal colleges and professional organisations was generally positive and they welcomed the introduction of national standard setting.

The notable dissenters were GPs who expressed almost complete dissatisfaction with the Charter. According to them, it had encouraged patients to take their rights for granted and to ignore their responsibilities. However, the response to the questionnaire from GPs was low (6 of 30) and may not reflect the views of GPs nationally although this negative opinion was also expressed by GPs who took part in the primary care focus group. The view expressed in their written evidence by the Association of Managers in General Practice may be a better reflection of the true story but it still confirms the general point:

> *The Association was involved in the original group discussions, launch and dissemination of information to managers in general practice. [There was a] consensus that the Patient's Charter has had a limited use because it was too patient focused which gave rise to increased patient expectations beyond the capability of the service to deliver.*

Strengths of the Charter

On the other hand, its strengths were that it had identified key standards and had acted as an educational tool for raising public and staff awareness of quality issues and standards. It allowed national comparisons to be made and was useful for some monitoring purposes. It had also identified patient needs and helped focus attention on them.

Health authorities identified two of its main strengths: the fact that it had encouraged greater awareness of patient and carer needs among staff; and that it had provided a set of standards or targets which could be monitored, thus enabling comparisons to be made with other authorities and providing a basis for improvements. Acute trusts valued the way the Charter had helped them identify priorities, set and maintain consistent standards, and also improve performance in certain areas. Two of them said that it had also helped them to put patients on the agenda in relation to access and the 'softer' quality issues.

Acute and community trusts were more likely to say that one of its strengths was that it helped them change the culture in their trust towards a user perspective. Examples given included greater emphasis on privacy and dignity and better individualised care through the named nurse concept. The community and mental health trusts said the Charter had raised patient and carer awareness of their rights and standards and that, in some cases, it had also raised staff awareness of patients' needs. It had also provided a tool for quality improvements in the physical environment (privacy and dignity).

The following quotation summarises most of the strengths they mentioned.

> *[The Patients Charter] has clarified what users of the service can expect from the NHS. It has to some degree addressed the issues around waiting lists/waiting times. It has encouraged innovative approaches to addressing some of the difficulties in demand within the NHS. It has defined measurable achievements. It has encouraged feedback from patients and service users as they are able to measure the service provided against the expectations raised by the Charter.*
>
> Community and mental health trust

The ambulance services indicated that they had found it useful in a number of ways: as a guide to patient expectations; in promoting in-house materials to address issues of patient dignity, privacy, religion and culture; and also for special needs, such as visual and hearing impairment. It had also reinforced the need for essential service developments, and acted as a framework for complaints management. The two commonest statements, however, were that the Charter had identified a basic standard to which ambulance trusts should perform and had raised awareness of what patients should expect.

> *It clearly identifies what the public can expect from the NHS in certain areas. It can be used as a tool to explain to staff both the obligations of our own service and how they relate to the rest of the NHS (e.g. all staff receive a copy of the revised Patient's Charter in 1996 and copies are given to new recruits). The reference to 'softer' standards – respect for dignity, privacy and religious and cultural beliefs, commitment to providing information and treatment, the right to have complaints investigated – has prompted debate on these areas, although this was starting to happen anyway.*
>
> Ambulance trust

Three of the six responding GPs said there were no strengths to the Charter. The other three said that it had been useful in setting ground rules and that it had been helpful in relation to hospital waiting times. The Association of Practice Managers said that it had:

> *raised awareness of quality issues and standards in primary care and shifted the focus onto patients.*

Chart A shows the main categories of strengths of the Charter identified by respondents in the survey.

Chart A Strengths of the Patient's Charter

- Raised awareness of patients' needs/issues/rights
- Helped with standard setting/identification of priorities
- Set standards for performance/comparison/performance review
- A tool for quality initiatives
- Useful for monitoring
- Useful for complaints management
- Useful emphasis on information provision

Providers and non-providers each placed different emphasis on the value of the Charter in raising awareness of patient issues and rights; it is natural for CHCs and voluntary organisations to take a different line from health authorities and trusts. However, apart from the first category in the chart, similar proportions of providers, CHCs, and voluntary organisations also mentioned these strengths in their responses and it is reassuring that there is a fair amount of agreement on them.

The findings from the focus groups with NHS managers and clinicians (see Chart 4 in Appendix 4) to some extent confirm the positive comments about the Charter in the written evidence. The focus groups with clinicians also confirmed the more negative feelings of clinicians illustrated in the written evidence from general practitioners.

Weaknesses of the Charter

Responses about the weaknesses of the Patient's Charter were much less restrained, and pointed out not only what the Charter did *not* do but also the difficulties it had created.

It was said to have raised patient and public expectations beyond the services' capacity to meet them, while creating confusion about those rights and expectations. It had also ignored staff needs and diverted resources from service and clinical priorities. Some respondents pointed out that it had ignored major issues such as clinical outcomes and the quality of the patient experience. The emphasis on acute services was seen as misguided by some respondents, as was the fact that its national standards were not always achievable locally.

Health authorities said that by focusing on waiting times, the Charter had distracted attention from clinical need which should have been the real priority.

> *Many of the standards do not focus on clinical need but on something else e.g. time waited. Also the standards may work against each other e.g. 12/18 months waited versus cancelled operations and may have a perverse effect on quality, e.g. triage in A&E, full assessment time (this should improve with the new standard).*
>
> Health authority

They also criticised the emphasis on quantitative standards or 'bean counting', as it was often described. These criticisms were echoed by acute trusts, acute and combined trusts and also by community and mental health trusts, whose most frequent comments related to the extra work involved in collecting the necessary statistics that were then often 'fudged'. The trusts were equally concerned with the way the Charter had raised patient expectations.

> *[The Charter has caused] confusion for public and staff alike between rights and expectations – and the public certainly regard expectations as rights! [It has caused] bureaucratic and time consuming monitoring requirements which are very problematic if data are not available from PAS or other minimum data set systems.*
>
> Acute trust

Criticisms of monitoring requirements and the quantitative aspects of the Charter included the fact that there was a lack of clarity and definition about many standards which led to extra work.

> *Weaknesses include the lack of clarity of definition. It should be in line with league table definitions so when collecting data it is only collected once and suffices both purposes, not collected in three different ways for three definitions [Körner, Patient's Charter, League Tables].*
>
> Acute and community trust

To summarise, the main thrust of criticisms by health authority and trusts fell within five categories:

- problems with charter standards
- emphasis on waiting times rather than clinical need
- emphasis on quantitative standards rather than quality of services and patient experience
- problems of monitoring
- patient expectations raised beyond the capacity of the services to deliver.

These categories also covered the comments made by other organisations, although the emphasis was sometimes different. Ambulance trusts, for example, said that the Patient's Charter failed to focus on clinical need and priorities. All six GP respondents felt its major weakness was that it had raised patients' expectations beyond GPs' capacity to meet them. No other weaknesses were mentioned. The royal colleges and professional organisations also commented about raised patient expectations which created a 'rights' mentality, and pointed to the desire for quantity not quality. CHCs and voluntary organisations mentioned raised patient expectations, problems with standards and too much emphasis on quantity, but they also include a wider range of comments about the special needs of specific client groups.

Chart B shows the major categories of complaints about the Charter.

Chart B Weaknesses of the Patient's Charter

- Problems with standards/lack of clarity/too narrow/wrong
- Difficulties with monitoring/collection of statistics
- Peoples' expectations raised too high/beyond the resources of the services to meet
- Ignores clinical need/outcomes
- Too much focus on quantity
- Too acute oriented
- No patient responsibilities included

One of the most interesting findings about the Charter is the discrepancy between patients' perceptions of it and NHS staff perceptions. On the one hand, patients in the focus groups knew little about the Charter, what it contained or how to use it; but, on the other hand, staff thought that patients' expectations had risen because of it and regarded this as pressure on them and a threat.

Priorities for quality in the NHS

Survey participants were asked to name the most important quality issue for their organisation: and *the quality of clinical outcomes* was identified more than any other. Altogether, six main categories were mentioned. Chart C identifies them.

Chart C Priorities for quality standards

- Clinical effectiveness
- Access to services/treatment
- User involvement/partnership
- Effective information/communication
- Staff training/qualified/staff attitudes/behaviour
- Quality of patient care including patient privacy/dignity/respect

Comments made by a handful of respondents which fell outside these categories included:

- volunteering
- continuity of care
- relationships with non-NHS organisations such as local authorities and voluntary organisations.

The emphasis changed in the responses to the next question which asked which standards should be included in a new Patient's Charter. Two new categories appeared:

- greater focus on community services, including primary care
- more focus on vulnerable care groups such as the mentally ill and groups which found access to care difficult, such as homeless people, refugees, elderly people, and minority ethnic groups.

Chart D lists priorities respondents felt should be included in a new Patient's Charter. It is arranged in order of popularity from the top down.

Chart D Quality standards for inclusion in a new charter

- Clinical effectiveness/outcomes
- Partnerships/involvement of patients in treatment and service planning
- Effective information and communication
- Access to services
- Community and primary care services
- The patient experience including privacy, dignity, and respect
- Staff training, qualifications and attitudes
- Focus on vulnerable groups

Some of the respondents here offered useful advice. One acute trust emphasised the need to include a clear statement about the purpose of the Charter because:

> *Clarity of purpose of the objectives and need for a charter. The press has already suggested that Britain has charters because it cannot provide the service. The current charter is a statement of standards for the NHS. Apart from the hard quantitative waiting times information, the other standards are not easily measurable. There are thousands of indicators and data sets that could be included in the new charter ... whatever is included should be achievable.*
>
> Acute trust

Actively involving patients or users and carers in their own treatments and in other aspects of services gained considerable support here:

> *Increased patient/user participation with service providers and users working in partnership with a greater emphasis on locally based services and agreed priorities for health service provision*
>
> Community mental health trust

was a sentiment supported by a third of all respondents.

Good systems of communication and information provision also received strong support:

> *Some aspects such as communication should be mandatory.*
>
> Community health council

Local communication systems [should be] established and monitored.

Community mental health trust

Vulnerable groups received special attention. One voluntary organisation recommended:

Listening to the views of older people and people with dementia and their families and friends and designing the services to meet their needs. Attention to the rights of vulnerable residents within homes and how their health care and rights of redress can be covered in the Charter.

Voluntary organisation

Another point made in several ways related to the special needs of ethnic groups and suggested that the new charter should include:

Provision of bi-lingual staff . . . provision of trained interpreters familiar with health jargon . . . training of all staff on religious, cultural practices, equal opportunities.

Voluntary organisation

It was not only voluntary organisations who made such points. In fact, there were proportionately more comments from provider trusts in this category. Non-provider organisations offered more comments in the 'access to services' category and the effective information and communication category and the emphasis on community and primary care category. One professional organisation said:

Continuity of care should be an objective of all health care providers; patients have the right to expect as seamless a transition as possible between different health care providers and between health and social services.

Royal college

This section reflects closely the evidence from the in-depth interviews and from the patient focus groups, although the NHS managers and clinicians in the written evidence gave as much emphasis to these priorities for a new charter as did voluntary organisations and patients' groups. Agreement on the agenda for the new charter appears to be spread across the divide, albeit with certain differences in emphasis.

Information needs

Respondents unanimously identified the need for information about conditions and treatments as being the most important information requirement of all.

> *People should be informed about the name of the condition, the prognosis, possible treatment and the way it is likely to affect their lives. This helps people come to terms with what is happening and what will happen in the future. It allows them to plan and organise and provides the basis for talking to others ... which may further their understanding and enables others to provide appropriate support.*
>
> Voluntary organisation

When asked what kinds of information were most useful to people using NHS services, the majority (two-thirds) identified clinical information about individual conditions and treatments.

> *If they are to be informed partners in their own health care, patients need clinical information; for example on what tests are being carried out, why, and their results; on why a certain intervention has been chosen or drugs have been prescribed and how they will work; on rehabilitation care and on what is expected of them and why.*
>
> Royal college

Drugs, medication, their effects, and reasons for prescribing them, were also mentioned.

The second most important information requirement was reckoned to be access to services.

> *First, people need information about how to access the NHS in an emergency or for routine care. As suggested in the Chief Medical Officer's Review of Emergency Care in the Community, they may need information to assist them in judging the nature and severity of their condition in order that they can make an informed decision about how to access the services.*
>
> Ambulance trust

The third most frequently mentioned information need was about standards of services and what could be expected of local services.

> *Information on what can realistically be expected within any given health situation. More comprehensive information to members of the public about services available in districts other than those in which they live. This would enable them to make choices.*
>
> Community mental health trust

Two other kinds of information requirements were mentioned with equal frequency. They were: information about non-NHS support services and organisations – self-help groups, for example, and complementary therapies. The other concerned staff qualifications, particularly of doctors. This information, it was felt, would assist patients and also allow GPs to exercise choice on their behalf.

Chart E shows the range of information that respondents felt should be available to patients and the public.

Chart E Information needs of patients and the public

- Conditions/treatment/medications with risks and benefits
- Access to services
- Standards of services
- Non-NHS support services
- Staff qualifications

The importance of providing this kind of information to patients and the public was supported by the literature review and the interviews with patient organisations.

National and local charters

The written evidence suggested that there was considerable support for a national charter that provided a framework of standards as well as local charters that were adapted to local conditions. Those who felt that there should be a national charter acting as a framework for local standards (over half the respondents) emphasised that the NHS is a national service and a national charter was essential to maintain this important concept and ensure equity throughout the country.

Given the diversity of cultures, languages, values and beliefs nationally I feel that a national framework backed up by local charters is the most valuable way forward. There is a strong feeling that this might be crucial in particular to the process of devolution.

Professional organisation

Although there was strong support for this approach, there were also worries that a proliferation of standards could lead to confusion.

As a national service we should have a national charter embodying standards that all citizens can expect to receive. Local charters can give scope to talk in more detail about specific populations and address local issues. They present the opportunity to lever up standards between areas. However, they may also lead to confusion in the minds of the public as do subject-specific charters.

Ambulance trust

The organisations which preferred just a national charter (a quarter of respondents) felt this was the only way to set strong standards and avoid a confusing plethora of local standards.

There should be one national charter to avoid local interpretation. Everyone, irrespective of where they live, should be entitled to the same basic standard of service. There should be nothing in this to prevent local services aiming to improve on the basic standards, particularly as the emphasis is now switching from competition to collaboration.

Community health council

There were three organisations who felt that there should be only local charters.

The reality for NHS users is the translation of the priorities and planning document, charter etc. into the trusts' business, purchaser quality specification, annual report, quality strategies and frameworks. Therefore, a local charter which combines these may be more informative to staff and public.

Acute trust

About a quarter of respondents had worked in areas which had local charters and their comments about the strengths and weaknesses of them obviously reflected their own experiences. One consistent theme was the importance of involving users in drafting the charter. Some people felt this had given patients and staff a sense of ownership and others mentioned that the process of collaboration was a valuable aspect of local charter development. It might also be possible to set higher standards locally than nationally, in addition to reflecting local needs and priorities which were perhaps more relevant than the national ones. This point was reiterated by NHS staff in the focus groups.

> *Our local charter has been very useful in involving users. It has raised expectations and, in turn, quality.*
>
> Managers' focus group

Conversely, local charters were criticised for 'loose' or 'woolly' standards, for confusing patients, for the cost in time and money of producing them and keeping them up to date, for the fact that no one used them 'despite wide publicity', for a bias towards acute services, and for a failure to monitor 'softer' standards. Ambulance services were unhappy because their areas sometimes involved several different local charters. They were particularly keen for collaboration between health authorities, purchasers and ambulance trusts to agree locally relevant performance targets related to emergency response times.

> *It would have been more helpful if the Charter had, for example, stated the need for the local health authority and ambulance trust to collaborate to reach 95 per cent of patients in x minutes, say. This approach would have concentrated more energy on the misuse of 999 services sooner than it has. In future the achievement of standards has to be a genuine shared responsibility between purchasers and providers, particularly when the maximum performance targets are not financially achievable.*
>
> Ambulance trust

Standards to be included in local charter

Respondents who supported a national charter framework backed up by local charters made a variety of suggestions about the necessary standards for a local charter. It was here that people commented on the need for charters to highlight ways in which resources limited services. National charter topics that should also be included in local charters were: access to services, waiting times and lists, and clinical standards.

Reference was also made to such specialist services as cardiac, cancer, palliative care, mental health and children's services. The need to include standards for special cases like minority ethnic groups and refugees was mentioned by several organisations.

> *A local charter would need to include provision of information in languages of the local community and the right to access to professionals in the NHS who speak the languages of the communities: respect for all religions and cultures.*
>
> Voluntary organisation

Some organisations mentioned the need to include information on staff training and professional development as well local voluntary organisations and carer groups. These suggestions are all relevant to local services and communities but there were also comments which gave the impression that people wanted something more like a local annual report than a charter. Remarks like: 'intentions against morbidity', 'cost comparisons between providers' and 'details of how national standards are to be met' indicated the wish for a more substantial document than a local charter could ever be. One health authority has already solved the problem:

> *Local charters should reflect how the national one has been interpreted locally: we adopt this method locally and report through annual reports.*
>
> Health authority

Given the amount of support for a national charter framework backed by local charters, this is probably the most appropriate and useful way forward for the future. The advantage here is that patients and local people who set the standards will incorporate their own views and experiences and also begin to understand some of the limitations of the service. Issues for them to confront will include allocation of time and money to draft the charter and how to relate local standards to the national ones. There is also the question of monitoring both local and national standards. One of the commonest complaints from NHS staff about the national charter was the difficulty of collecting and presenting good quality information about its standards. Although the need for local as well as national standard setting is clear, it may not be easy to achieve.

Publicity for a new Patient's Charter

Most suggestions about publicity for a new charter fell into one of three main categories:

- national and local press
- NHS services
- information posted in public places.

Respondents often suggested a combination of all three. However, the most favoured method was a launch through either the national media or through both national and local media: media here includes TV, radio, newspapers and magazines (two-thirds of respondents mentioned these sources). In contrast, about a quarter of respondents preferred direct publicity towards targeted audiences through clinics, GP surgeries, and hospitals because a large amount of money had been wasted sending the previous charter to all households, and yet few people (or patients)were even aware of its existence.

> *The first charter was meant to go to every home – an expensive exercise that nonetheless did not lead to the widespread knowledge that might have been hoped for. A press campaign at the launch and wide availability of the Charter at all places that health care is delivered would probably be better.*
>
> Ambulance trust

Few respondents felt it should again be delivered to all households. About a third said it should be available at places such as libraries, council offices, job centres, cinemas, market stalls and post offices and should be advertised with posters, wall charts and leaflets in NHS clinics, surgeries and hospitals, as well as on buses and at bus stops. A few people felt there was scope for using the Charter publicity to educate children and young people to stay healthy. Several organisations mentioned the need to find a way of publicising the Charter to ethnic groups and others, such as people with visual and hearing impairments. It was pointed out that the most effective form of publicity was to involve people in the development of the Charter.

One sceptic said that the whole idea of a chart should be scrapped to save money, and another reckoned that it should not be called a charter. One respondent advised:

> *Charter fatigue is a real problem: any new charter will face a wall of 'been there, done that' attitude. It is essential therefore, to make it fresh in form as well as substance. Public involvement in the NHS must be improved; there has to be public involvement with the charters and their implementation.*
>
> Royal college

There were several suggestions that TV soap operas could be used to generate publicity and one person put forward the idea that 'charter champions', well-known personalities, might be persuaded to convey the Charter messages to the public.

Suggestions for publicising the Charter within the NHS included:

- staff training/cascade methods
- information in in-house magazines and professional journals
- internal briefings with discussion and guidance
- building charter standards into performance reviews of both staff and the organisation.

Other suggestions included placing leaflets or handouts in pay packets; putting messages on internal e-mails; leaving materials in staff rooms and lockers; involving staff in charter development; and building it into the culture of the organisation.

Encouraging effective use of NHS services by patients, carers and the public

Many NHS managers and clinicians were dissatisfied with what they perceived to be irresponsible use of services by patients. The survey invited them to suggest ways patients could be encouraged to use services responsibly and the problems they may encounter in meeting these responsibilities. Chart F indicates how respondents felt this could be accomplished.

Chart F Patients' contribution to better working relationships with NHS staff

- Change behaviour
- Keep appointments and notify cancellations
- Use services properly
- Take responsibility for own health
- Improve communication

The chart illustrates that the main contribution patients could make would be to change their behaviour. Comments in this category related primarily to good manners; that is, being polite, demonstrating mutual respect (patients for staff and staff for patients), and acknowledging that staff were human, too. Strong feelings were expressed about patient and carer abuse of staff with occasional acts of violence, accompanied by a wish that sanctions might be used against people who behaved in this way.

Keeping appointments, punctuality and telephoning cancellations was the second most frequently mentioned category of bad behaviour, although CHCs and voluntary organisations did not mention this as often as did NHS staff.

Third on the list was the misuse of services and included three comments from ambulance trusts who were concerned about inappropriate call-outs for 999 services:

> *This is an important area for ambulance services as we find that many of our callers seek help for conditions that are not urgent.*

Other providers who made similar comments emphasised, however, that people needed information to use these services properly.

There was a handful of comments about the responsibility of people to keep themselves healthy. The category labelled 'communication' should properly be included under changing behaviour but was isolated because it focused on the need for staff and patients to improve channels of communication in both directions, whereas the behaviour category was almost entirely about the way patients behaved. The follow-up question to this asked what problems people might have in meeting their responsibilities to NHS services. Unexpectedly, there was much less 'blaming' of patients here and, instead, important areas were identified where the NHS could be changed to help patients deliver those responsibilities.

Chart G indicates that the two main categories covered poor information and lack of understanding (that is, problems with communication) along with NHS system problems; these were areas where changes could be made to encourage responsible use of services.

Chart G The problems that patients have in meeting their responsibilities to the NHS

- Lack of information and understanding along with poor communication
- Problems with NHS systems
- Public and patient perceptions that need changing
- Problems with society as a whole

The largest category covered patients who had little understanding of the way NHS services worked and the limitations on them. It also included the difficulties people have understanding their conditions and treatment, which often prevents them from following professional advice. The following sympathetic comment from a community and mental health trust illustrates some of the difficulties faced by both patients and staff:

> *This [meeting responsibilities] is an extremely complex problem which deserves a thesis! A succession of governments has failed to address the class divide, poverty, elitism and human frailty. I sincerely hope that one day we can sufficiently empower people so they feel valued and, in turn, value themselves and their environment. Education in the broadest sense is a key to problem solving and facing responsibilities.*
>
> Community and mental health trust

The second category related to problems with NHS systems and included difficulties of accessing out-of-hours services and getting through telephone switchboards to cancel appointments. It also covered the mistakes which are sometimes made in recording attendance so that what was a cancellation turns into a 'did not attend'; lack of resources to deliver services adequately; staff attitudes under pressure and the need for training to help them deal with patients.

The third category included the need to change patient and public perceptions, the fact that expectations had risen too high for services to meet, and anxieties about using services along with fear of illness.

> *People are afraid and vulnerable when attending clinics or when being admitted for treatment; therefore they feel they cannot challenge the system or do not know what questions to ask. Some people feel if they complain it will affect the care they are given.*
>
> Acute and community trust

Problems in society included poverty, difficulties with public transport in reaching services, an increasing level of aggression, lack of respect for people and property ... all were cited by at least one respondent as reasons why people might be prevented from meeting their responsibilities to the NHS. Of course, it is not within the power of the NHS to do anything about problems of this kind.

The written evidence was weighted towards NHS managers and providers although CHCs and voluntary organisations were well represented and it was reassuring to find that all respondents made a similar range of comments although the emphasis was often different. This section of the research offered a useful critique of the existing Charter and gave positive contributions about the form and content of any new one.

Appendix 4

Focus groups with patients, managers and clinicians

This appendix reports on the findings from a series of focus groups of NHS clinicians, managers, patients and carers. They discussed their experiences of the existing Charter and how they would like it to evolve into a new one.

Awareness of the Charter and views about its purpose

Awareness of the Charter

Managers and clinicians were much more familiar with the Patient's Charter and its contents than were patients. Despite their greater familiarity with the principles of the Charter and its impact, many found it necessary, however, to refresh their memories about the document itself just prior to attending the focus groups.

Patients' commonest response when asked about the Charter was that they had heard of it but were not sure what it contained. When pushed, patients usually revealed some awareness of the idea behind the Charter but lacked any clear understanding of its contents. This tallies with National Opinion Poll (1994) findings about patients' low awareness of the Charter.

> *[I know] the Charter in part, just bits and pieces. You don't have to wait for treatment, you can complain if you have to wait so long.*

NHS professionals, asked whether *they* felt patients were aware of the Charter, said that patients' awareness was usually either fragmentary or inaccurate.

> *People might know there's a charter, but I don't know they always know what's in it. I think people know about 30-minute outpatient waits. I don't think a lot of health service managers know about all of it.*
>
> Managers

Sources of information about the Charter

Few patients recalled receiving a Patient's Charter leaflet. Any references to the Charter they had seen were either in the form of league tables in the press, or in local hospital waiting rooms: it was all haphazard. Often, the Charter was associated with hospitals rather than primary care services.

> *I was under the impression that the Patients' Charter only came into operation when you were actually in the hospital … because I have only ever seen it in hospitals. I have never seen it in surgeries.*
>
> Banbury

> *It seems a bit strange that none of us know what it is. It's not up on any notice boards and you don't see it in the media. It makes you think they don't want people to quibble.*
>
> Manchester

This lack of awareness of the Charter is perhaps to be expected. Research on information about health care issues suggests that people are only interested in it and retain the information when they actually need it. Indeed, patients themselves said much the same thing.

> *But that is like everything with the National Health, or any similar organisation. You don't get to know about it until you actually use the system, whether it be personally or whether it be through your family.*
>
> Banbury

Opinions on the aims of the Charter

When participants discussed the *explicit* reasons for introducing the Charter, there was apparent scepticism about the motives behind it. Although this scepticism was reflected commonly among professionals, it was also felt by the patients' groups.

Clinicians and managers, for instance, said they found it difficult to take 'ownership' of the Charter as its specific purpose had remained ambiguous from the outset and its perceived priorities did not necessarily coincide with their own.

Positive Charter aims identified by them are outlined in Chart 1.

Chart 1 Clinicians' and managers' views of the positive purposes of the Charter

To clarify standards for both staff and patients by:

- providing a set of national standards for the NHS
- providing a set of explicit standards that service providers could work towards
- defining what people could expect from the NHS (e.g. waiting times)

To monitor and be more open about NHS performance by:

- creating an explicit statement about the public accountability of the NHS
- publishing performance statistics and providing more information about NHS performance
- creating a performance measurement tool to use within the NHS as the basis for contracting services and monitoring service delivery

To empower patients and move the service forward by:

- making patients' rights as service users more explicit and inviting them to comment on the service

A repeated comment was that this was an attempt to improve quality in the NHS without any serious analysis of the situation, without consulting staff or patients, and with no resources to support such improvements.

> *It felt like a political move, so that the Government could demonstrate some form of quality going on in a service which didn't necessarily reflect the real issues on the ground as far as quality was concerned. It felt like a political move rather than any real commitment to improving quality.*
>
> Managers

Others believed the Charter was essentially negative and an instrument with which to beat staff.

> *A cynical view, particularly in this part of the service, was that a lot of initiatives were about identifying who to blame when things go wrong. The Patient's Charter was seen very much in that context as well, that here were things that didn't measure anything of any real importance. It was something that they could beat people with at some stage in the future.*
>
> Managers

It was also suggested that the Charter was one aspect of a broader move to limit the power of doctors.

> *The Government did have this issue about the consultants and about medical power and so on and what they were doing was using this issue of patients' expectations to put that message across to the doctors. It's probably a good ploy in itself and that's why the Patient's Charter is full of ambiguous language.*
>
> Managers

Patients' views of the aims of the Charter

Patients' feelings about the Charter's aims overlapped with the views of NHS professionals, but were based on speculations about what it might contain.

Positive aspects they identified are summarised in Chart 2.

Chart 2 Positive views from patients about the purpose of the Charter

- To improve service quality and choice, in keeping with the initiative set by the Citizens' Charter
- To demonstrate the performance of the service against a number of established targets
- To ensure a more equitable distribution of NHS resources by setting out a framework of patients' rights and the basic service provision to which they should be entitled, regardless of where they live or their ability to pay
- To give patients the freedom to complain or to question NHS staff if they feel their rights have been infringed
- To provide a means of monitoring the service as a routine management tool

Like staff, patients also felt these aims were not the real reason for introducing the Charter and doubted, in some cases, any commitment to follow through on them. They asked if it had really enabled patients to exercise their rights effectively and questioned the political will to implement any such rights.

> *I should think it's something to do with us having quality and choice and that kind of carry on as with the Citizens' Charter. It's full of very pious words, [but] I should think the reality's far away from that. If you can cry 'Off with their heads!' if they don't perform perhaps it would work, but in my position where I do want to make a complaint and it's going to take me a long time to find a doctor that's going to take me before I can feel safe to make that complaint. There's no structure there for complaints.*
>
> Walthamstow

Perceptions and experiences of the Charter in action

This section explores perceptions and experiences of the Charter and is drawn largely from NHS managers and clinicians; patients themselves had little experience of it.

Staff views and initial expectations

Some of the managers and clinicians had hoped that the Charter would be a constructive way to move the service forward by establishing targets and feedback mechanisms. These hopes were largely dashed. Staff felt it had not worked in practice because:

- Charter standards were irrelevant
- there was a negative and 'biased' tone to the Charter
- there were negative reactions to the way in which it was created and implemented
- there was a lack of forethought about its repercussions and how they could be addressed

Lack of relevance

For example, the Charter was thought to have neglected mental health and learning disability services. Staff who were originally keen on the Charter later lost interest in it.

Another common theme was that it simply failed to coincide with the priorities of either staff or patients.

> *It didn't connect with our agenda and our perceptions of either our needs or our patients' needs…*
>
> Primary care

Many professionals had hoped the Charter would help improve the quality of what the NHS offered, but instead they felt that it had focused on issues which were easily measured, which were perhaps less important to patients and staff.

> *It never actually looked at the care and it was never meant to and I think that was the most frustrating to clinicians because from a clinician's point of view, it wasn't measuring what we perceived to be quality.*
>
> Clinician

The Charter seemed 'biased'

It was felt that the Charter was biased towards patients at the expense of staff. It offered patients rights with no corresponding responsibilities. This was particularly difficult for staff to accept at a time when verbal and physical assaults on them are increasing.

> *It's all very one-sided and patients, and particularly relatives, have become very aggressive towards nursing staff.*
>
> Clinicians

Staff felt that the Charter actively encouraged patients to complain about NHS services while ignoring other types of feedback.

> *A lot of people feel there is an emphasis on complaining rather than commenting or complimenting. All it needed to say was if you want to make comments on the service this also covers compliments. But I know a lot of the staff feel that patients are almost encouraged to complain, which isn't a bad thing, but it is difficult when you're struggling with a busy clinic.*
>
> Managers

Negative reactions to how the Charter was created and implemented

Another recurrent discontent with the Charter concerned the way that it was introduced without proper consultation, which was also reflected in comments about the mismatch of its standards with the priorities of patients' and staff. It was said that some of the standards are 'unrealistic' or 'unachievable'.

> *It's something that's imposed on us and without consultation at the beginning. It was imposed from above and very little works with that approach. The Mental Health Charter came out, as I remember, from consultation after a lot of us made an awful fuss. And we all wrote to them about it and not one single thing was taken into account, which is pretty irritating when you've taken the time to go through it with a fine-toothed comb.*
>
> Managers

Putting the Charter's recommendations into practice brought blame on service providers especially if standards were not met and increased hostility towards it.

What went wrong is that sticks were attached to it. It was policed, and people started running round pretty pointlessly, in my view. If it hadn't been imposed to the same degree if people had said: 'These are the standards to which we think you should aspire', without ringing up people in the middle of the night, you know, hiring and firing. That was very negative, very negative, got the whole thing a bad name.

Clinicians

Staff also noted that although they were told to meet the new Charter standards, they were given little support or direction on how to do this and seldom further resources for the task.

Lastly, people felt that this situation raised patients' expectations unrealistically and unfairly.

I think the idea was good, but the problem which we face is the gap between the patients' expectations and exactly what's happening on the ground. And it was a bit unfortunate that patients and clinicians were being given a very false impression about what the Patient's Charter was going to achieve. And, of course, that's created a lot of problems. There are very limited resources to try to achieve the Patient's Charter, and I feel any discussion will have to be more realistic and try to address the issue – what can you actually afford?

Clinicians

Staff views and experiences of the Charter standards

The weight of staff opinion about standards was largely negative for a number of reasons. Problems occurred on two fronts: with the standards themselves and with the management and implementation of them. These difficulties have created increased pressure on staff, which has led to negative reactions to the Charter itself.

However, there were some charter standards which staff agreed were positive: the outpatient waiting time of 30 minutes and the six-week time allowance for the transfer of patient records. These led to a better service for patients and staff without compromising other service standards.

Problems with the standards themselves

Staff experiences with the standards indicated four areas of difficulty:

- unsuitable for the complexity of the service
- unrealistic or unachievable standards in the current service
- failure to address issues of quality
- encouragement of 'distortion' of the service.

Unsuitable for the complexity of the service

To begin with, standards seemed to promote discrete aspects of service provision without recognising their inter-dependence on one another. A common example of this was the length of time taken from decision to admit to actual admission from accident and emergency departments. This standard concentrates solely on the access point to the service, the A&E Department, but admission from such departments is dependent on a number of other service areas (e.g. the ward which will receive the patient and the availability of beds and administrative support responsible for matching beds to places). The standard concerns itself with only one part of a larger system, while other parts of the system remain unscrutinised.

> *They asked for trolley waiting times. I've been collecting trolley waiting times for years now and we know where the problem comes in: there isn't a bed. What chance do you have with your general public who quite reasonably complain that they're on a trolley for four hours? It's not because we want them on the trolley, it's because we can't move them anywhere else.*
>
> Clinicians

A second contention is that the standards focus disproportionately on specific aspects of service provision, while largely ignoring others. This has led to the belief that the Charter has a patchy approach and does not follow the patient properly through the system.

> *In terms of mental health services, the kinds of standards around time scales are totally irrelevant for mental health. Adult learning disability is another issue. We've developed local charters for those services because the national charter failed to recognise those issues at all. In fact, I feel the national charter was based entirely on acute services as if nothing else existed.*
>
> Managers

Unrealistic or unachievable in the current service context

Staff were also frustrated with targets because it was unrealistic to apply national standards uniformly across very different local settings. In particular, there were problems with standards which focus on percentages without reference to volumes and make no allowance for areas of greater demand. The ambulance service was another example in which geographical differences do not appear to have been taken into account when setting standards for transport times.

Difficulties with the original five-minute triage time in A&E were mentioned to illustrate the point that staff who deliver the service are in the best position to set realistic targets and would welcome more consultation on this in future.

> *I think one of the disadvantages or the drawbacks of the existing charter is that it doesn't take locality into account in terms of trying to deliver a service. Geography and general environmental conditions will have a major effect [on the Ambulance Service]. To try and apply a national standard makes this very difficult to achieve across the board.*
>
> Managers

Failure to address issues of quality

A persistent theme with clinicians and managers was that the current standards do not adequately address issues of quality. They concentrate on what is easily measured rather than what really matters to patients and staff in terms of patient well-being and service excellence. Achievement of the standard sometimes leads to a poor quality of service. Staff felt that measuring the time spent waiting to get access to the service was less important than the quality of service provided. Current standards tend to concern themselves less with the quality of patients' experiences than with time taken for access and to move from one part of the service to another.

> *It's focused on what you can measure relatively easily and some of those things don't necessarily reflect the quality of the service. Measuring cancelled operations is fine but it doesn't talk about quality.*
>
> Managers

Encouraging distortion of the service

A combination of the preceding factors, plus issues of management and implementation, have led to a situation in which managers and clinicians worry that adherence to the standards leads to distortion of the service and deviation from other established priorities. Specific concern was expressed regarding the conflict between prioritising access to the service according to clinical need and the standard which guarantees a wait of no more than 18 months for operations.

In addition, other standards suggest that there is always a 'best' way to approach health care. This does not allow for local circumstances and also patients' own priorities, which may mean that following standard procedure results in a less favourable situation for the patient. The standard may interfere with a clinician's ability to make decisions which are in the patient's best interest.

> *Surely the priority of the day is determined on the basis of clinical need of each patient who comes in, and I think the Charter has actually interfered with that to a certain extent, which is really bad news for the patient and it's exceptionally bad news for us because of all the training we have undertaken in order to be able to prioritise according to patients' needs.*
>
> Clinicians

> *The Patient's Charter is very clear on the one named nurse, but I could think of some excellent team nursing approaches that work very well. If you go strictly by the wording of the Patient's Charter, that does not fit in yet it provides the patient with exactly what they want.*
>
> Clinicians

The spirit versus the letter of the Charter

There were some staff who had more favourable views of the Charter because it had been implemented along with other measures designed to improve quality within their area. Standards were, therefore, valuable (though with refinements) because they were part of a broader package of quality initiatives. In other areas, meeting the targets appeared to be an end in itself and staff described this as a paperchase rather than a genuine attempt to use the information gathered to assess progress and move the service forward.

> *My staff would say the centre of their life has become standards. You get into long discussions on: when do you start your standard? From the phone call? From when you know it's an emergency? Do you round the 19 minutes up or down? They spend an awful lot of time concentrating on the standard and when [one] standard improves, all the other standards drop, so you end up chasing standards without, as my staff will tell you, any reference to what good it does the patient.*
>
> Managers

Lack of support for staff

Staff felt pressurised to monitor and meet the standards and said there was a tendency to apportion blame for failure to meet the targets. Some staff had the additional pressure of dealing with disappointment and complaints from patients themselves.

> *If it was a genuine management tool to review performance and which was linked to resources to do a reasonable job, it would be fine because then there would be adjustments and the money would be targeted fairly in the system. But that's clearly not been happening. People have had little injections to do this and that, or they've had to do it anyway, to manoeuvre figures around, and so it's not a uniformly audited and regulated management tool across the whole – it's not a level playing field.*
>
> Clinicians

This type of strain is counter-productive as it discouraged some staff from striving to make further improvements:

> *There's no incentive to improve because [I'll] achieve what is acceptable to my chief exec and once I've achieved that, I'm not going to get any better because it's a rod for my own back. I know I've got to maintain that percentage, whatever, so I'll achieve something which I know he's happy with and then that's all I will do. So I won't then try and improve upon that.*
>
> Clinicians

Monitoring the Charter

Staff in the focus groups noted a number of problems with monitoring the Patient's Charter standards. Four key issues emerged:

- an inadequate infrastructure to support the monitoring exercise
- a number of potential difficulties with the reliability of the data produced
- inadequate tools to measure quality
- inadequate mechanisms to feed back the monitoring results into performance review.

Inadequate infrastructure

Staff lacked appropriate information technology to support monitoring activities and often had to rely on manual methods which were time-consuming. It was a frustrating and onerous task and they were concerned about the quality of the data as well as the time spent away from clinical work.

> *We felt in our department that we were actually detracting from patient care because we were spending so much time trying to sort out the figures and then subsequently, dealing with the complaints. And that was sucking us away from the work that we were really supposed to be doing, which was treating the patients in the first place – very frustrating.*
>
> Clinicians

Reliability of the data produced

Staff also queried reliability of the data. They felt that under pressure they sometimes did not give priority to the monitoring. They also mentioned that those who thought the standards were irrelevant or unachievable would not concern themselves with monitoring. The data may therefore be based on an incomplete profile of clinical episodes.

> *We do sampling for the thirty minute outpatients because we don't have to do them all, and they are sampled, I'm sure, by those clinics that achieve that. And there are some consultants who have refused to be part of that sample because they say it's not achievable.*
>
> Managers

Additionally, staff felt that the data probably were not comparable between different locations. This was a recurrent issue as it was felt that, despite external audits, measurements were not being made identically in different locations. The way figures are calculated has changed since the introduction of the Charter, which implies that the data collected under such changes cannot be compared over time.

[Take] cancelled operations: when that originally came out it was simply that every cancelled operation was to be reported. But I noticed a short while ago that a new definition arrived, which allows a postponement, and if you see somebody within 24 hours that's not a cancellation, it's a postponement – so everybody's figures got better. When you have things like this happening, it's not surprising people can't take it seriously.

Clinicians

Lastly, they repeatedly described being put under pressure to produce acceptable figures and used words like *fudged* and *fiddled* in this regard.

When we present results to our purchasers, they regularly come back and say, 'We can't print these, we can't pass these figures on. Can't you give us something that is better?'

Clinicians

Inadequate tools to measure quality

Another concern was the quantitative exercise of gathering statistics to measure the standards, despite the fact that some issues in the Charter such as dignity and privacy for patients cannot be measured in this way.

Inadequate mechanisms to feed back the monitoring results into performance review

In some areas, staff felt that the information gathered was used only for external purposes and did not contribute to performance review within their own organisation.

The impact of the Patient's Charter

Encouragingly, despite the many problems staff have identified with the Charter, there are positive impacts which it has had on the service.

More efficient service delivery

Managers and clinicians felt that the Charter had definitely improved the speed of service in a few areas. Specific examples were: reduced waiting times in outpatients, making doctors be punctual in their outpatient clinics; reducing the time taken for the transfer of patients' records.

More patient focused

Staff said there had been a cultural shift in the way services were provided with more emphasis now on giving priority to patients' needs and expectations. Although the Charter was not solely responsible for these changes, it was one of a range of initiatives which helped to produce them. There was, for example, more information given to patients about services, more regular attempts to gather patient feedback, more emphasis on the patient as customer, more positive 'customer care' practices, and more priority given to patients' needs than in the past.

> *The nursing staff and outpatients are now aware of the patient. I think in the past it's very much been focused on the consultant, and an element of it has been protecting the consultant from the patients. I think it's changed round now and most people are aware that the patient's time is as important as the consultant's time.*
>
> Managers

The counter-point to these positive views is that the Charter has in some ways stifled communication between patients and service providers. For example, hospitals now seem reluctant to send information about future appointments to patients if this involves considerable delays. Primary care specialists felt that hospitals do not want to admit to long waiting times and instead delay sending letters about appointments until a month or six weeks before they are due. This may leave patients waiting several months for their next appointment and create anxiety for them at having been 'lost in the system'.

> *Our local hospital has got into the habit of not sending out anything until about four to six weeks before the appointment. So if you have got a seven or eight month waiting list to see someone, the patients are coming back [to the GP] in two to three months time saying: I haven't heard from the hospital. And that costs us an awful lot of man-hours in ringing people just to make sure that their letter has not fallen through the system somewhere. I suspect this is a direct result of the Patient's Charter because the hospital will actually avoid putting people on the waiting lists.*
>
> Primary care group

More creative solutions

Although staff objected to being forced to make improvements with meagre additional resources they still found this a challenge that required them to think more creatively and co-operatively about their approach to service delivery. Thus departments have been reorganised, more teamwork and co-ordinated effort among professionals from different disciplines has been generated, and there has even been a real interest in exploring complaints constructively and addressing the fundamental issues that cause problems.

> *One of the positive things that I've seen come out of it with quite a large group of surgeons who have worked individually up until very recently is the Patient's Charter has forced our hands to get together and we've certainly improved equity of admission for elective procedures. And I think there are more fair and just decisions being made about when these patients come into hospital now, partly as a result of managing the bed usage throughout the service rather than on an individual consultant's patch, which is how it used to be.*
>
> Clinicians

These reactions were not universally encountered, however, and resulted from the positive response shown by sections of the nursing and medical staff. Conversely, there were those who questioned whether the reorganisation in their own areas actually represented progress for the service.

Trade-offs between charter standards and 'quality'

Staff felt that the Charter did not actually address service quality. For many there was much greater emphasis on access to and delivery of services, which detracted from the more important issue of quality.

Trade-offs included:

- moving people quickly through the system, rather than improve the care that they receive, especially when the Charter standard is regarded as the goal
- diversion of resources from clinical care to Charter monitoring exercises
- indecision about priority: treat people according to clinical need or follow Charter standard on waiting times?

The question here is: are staff forced to jettison quality in order to pursue the more limited aspirations indicated in the Charter?

Staff are concerned about the conflict between their professional responsibility to treat according to clinical need and the simultaneous management drive to meet the Charter's standards. This is compounded by the claim in the Charter that patients have the right:

> *to receive health care on the basis of your clinical need, not on your ability to pay, your lifestyle or any other factor.*

This highlights the difficulty staff face working with standards which set maximum waiting times of 18 months for operations, regardless of clinical need.

> *I think the waiting list initiative has been a major problem in surgery. My acute admissions get first beds in the morning because we keep them overnight and then ward them in the morning to create beds for the next day. But as soon as the bed manager arrives, although we've booked the beds, the bed manager will come and say, 'This is a 12-month waiter, this patient has got to get in the bed before your acute'. And it's the acute patients who always seem to come second to the 12-month waiters, and the hospital can be full, not a bed in the hospital, but the 12-month waiters have got to get in.*
>
> Clinicians

The charter and a wider focus on quality

Generally, managers were more positive than clinicians about the potential of the Charter to improve quality within the service. Some managers saw it as a way to open discussion about where and how the service could be improved. These managers were perhaps the same ones who wanted to move beyond narrow standard-setting and use the Charter as part of a constructive feedback mechanism. The emphasis on standards, however, gave them leverage to influence members of staff who are resistant to change and who prefer traditional practices.

> *There's no doubt that when you create a core activity around quality, other things spin off from it regularly. I mean you don't just talk about catering standards or about 30-minute waits, you talk about those events that lead up to it or around it, so there is a view, and I think I support it, that it has been a useful vehicle to actually get the broader issue of quality clearly focused.*
>
> Managers

Conversely, some clinicians felt that the Charter imposes its own interpretation of quality which does not represent quality at all.

> *I work within the bounds of the quality directorate and just having that name to your job creates difficulties because people perceive 'quality' as the Patient's Charter and they rubbish the Patient's Charter and therefore they rubbish 'quality'. So any initiatives you try that are about the quality issues that we as clinicians are concerned about almost get lost because you're seen as somebody who's just trying to take the Government's quality agenda forward instead of the clinicians'.*
>
> Clinicians

Relationships between staff and patients

The Charter was said to have had differing effects on the relationship between staff and patients. On the one hand, there were staff who felt that their relationship with patients was strained because of more complaints about the service: these were sometimes aggressive and difficult to handle effectively, particularly with demanding workloads.

On the other hand, some staff (less commonly) thought the relationship had improved. They believed this had resulted from increased communication with patients and greater awareness of their needs.

Relationships between members of staff

When asked directly whether the Charter had affected relationships between members of NHS staff, the resounding reply was that it had made them more strained. Staff at all levels, both managers and clinicians, found themselves under pressure from all sides and said that blame for any difficulties with the Charter was passed through the ranks in a detrimental fashion.

> *I think it's impacted on the relationship between clinicians and management [they are] browbeaten to produce the right information and to change the systems and to make it work better, to drive it.*
>
> Clinicians

Staff also described a move towards greater teamwork and co-ordination efforts in an attempt to meet Charter standards, which implies that the effects on staff relationships were not entirely negative and indeed, in some areas, closer or more effective working may have developed.

Working lives of staff

Comments from staff about the effect of the Charter on their everyday working lives were largely negative. They said it had brought an increased workload they felt was a distraction from their 'real' professional duties. This was a particularly sore points with clinicians. In addition, the implementation of the Charter with no real increase in resources had left some staff feeling trapped between clamouring patients and the commands of managers and purchasers of services. Pressures on staff had now increased, and had made work less satisfying. Clinicians were also concerned that the Charter had impinged on their ability to focus on professional excellence; This is related to the sometimes unqualified nature of the rights now bestowed on patients, which appear to remove clinicians' discretion to act according to professional experience.

> *I would say the measures of quality are crude and they understate the excellence of the staff, and I think a lot of us feel de-professionalised by some of the extremely crude things that appear in patient's charters.*
>
> Clinicians

Impact on patients

How has the Patient's Charter affected patients themselves? Unfortunately, those patients who attended the focus groups had no great experience with it, so we asked staff for their opinion of the effect on patients. They said there were some ways that patients had been helped by it, which included:

- encouraging greater patient awareness among NHS staff
- reducing waiting times in outpatients
- providing more information to patients about the service
- arranging quicker access to services.

These are principally objective changes but there were also more subjective ones staff had observed in patients' attitudes which they attributed, at least in part, to the Charter. These included:

- higher expectations of the service
- a greater feeling of justification in making complaints
- increased aggression towards staff which reflects wider social changes but may also be linked to rights in the Charter
- viewing the NHS less as a charity and more as a service paid for by customers.

Staff feel these changes in attitude have led to increased complaints from patients since the introduction of the Charter. Although they generally regard this as a negative development (it obstructs their own workload), some admitted that the service may become more responsive because of those complaints.

However, there was concern that patients may ultimately suffer because of the Charter if service providers focus more on meeting its targets than on their needs. Lastly, there were staff who felt that all patients may not benefit equally from the Charter and that a more articulate minority may gain more from it than others.

Overall assessments of the Charter's impact

There were marked differences in the views of managers and clinicians in their overall assessment of the impact of the Charter. Managers were quite positive, while clinicians were concerned about the detrimental effects they felt it had had.

Managers' views of the Charter's impact

Managers highlighted improvements to the service which they associated with the Patient's Charter, and although these were not necessarily a result of the Charter alone, they could see its potential for creating progress if the approach was right. If the Charter was used to improve quality throughout the service, for monitoring progress, and for involving patients in their own treatment, they felt it could be a vehicle for positive change. However, they pointed out that the Charter could have a negative effect where it was viewed solely as a meaningless 'box ticking' exercise.

Some of the positive effects which managers felt the Charter had helped to produce included:

- making performance measurement an issue of importance
- creating greater equity for areas where standards apply
- enabling a change in traditional practices which were not in patients' best interests
- increasing investment in staff by providing training in customer care skills
- increasing the importance placed on patients' opinions and involving them more collaboratively in treatment.

Clinicians' views of the Charter's impact

Clinicians felt the Charter did not provide quality in the service and could detract from it instead. The main difference between their view and that of managers was that managers were satisfied with changes in NHS practices but clinicians wanted more focus on the quality of clinical care given to patients. They described the Charter as superficial, irrelevant and potentially dangerous, especially if it created conflicts between addressing clinical need and meeting its own standards. Although they acknowledged there were positive aspects to it, their overall assessment was that it had little impact at all, or even a negative impact by diverting resources from more useful ways of addressing quality. Among points they raised in connection with this were:

- it diverted resources from other quality initiatives already in place when the Charter was introduced
- it diverted money and resources from initiatives to improve health care to the monitoring of standards
- it obscured and interfered with issues of clinical need and priority
- it failed to optimise the quality of the system as a whole and focused only on isolated bits of the service
- it promoted a situation where patients' needs may be viewed as secondary to the achievement of charter standards
- it failed to promote respect between patients and clinicians by emphasising rights without responsibilities.

Towards a new charter for the NHS

Although patients and NHS staff understand and experience the service from different angles, there is much common ground on which to build a new charter.

What is the Charter for?

Patients' perspectives

Patients felt there were positive aspects to the Charter (as outlined in Chapter 2), but there was a minority view that the Charter itself did not confer rights on patients. Instead, it was felt that patients have always had rights as service users, whether or not they were explicitly granted, and the Charter should not be used as a means for limiting people's rights to those issues specified in the document.

There's a danger that it could actually be used to restrict one's rights and your rights would be limited to what's on this bit of paper. I think it needs to be dealt with on a much more fundamental and flexible basis.

Manchester

However, if the Charter helped people who feel they have no rights in the NHS to understand that they do, then this was seen as an important contribution it could make to society. In this sense, the Charter would not offer a restricted list of rights, but would simply indicate fundamental rights to which all users were entitled.

I think you have to assume that the general public has no idea what to expect and what their rights are on the NHS. Even if the Charter helps, 5 per cent of people to realise that they do have rights within the NHS, then surely it's helped those 5 per cent to push [for those rights].

Walthamstow

In discussing how patients regarded the difference between 'rights' and 'expectations' in the Charter, a number of points emerged. First, there was a basic question about whether patients have any rights at all and this is related to the greater issue of rights in a system which seems to offer few choices and limited powers of redress.

It's not a privilege this health service of ours, we've paid for it, but it's sort of doled out in precious little dollops to us. Fundamentally, it seems we've gone away from [the view] that we've got a health service for all our population and it's our right to it. Money is terribly tight and you're terribly privileged even to get this little bit.

Walthamstow

Patients did not say whether they felt the Charter should be aspirational, but did talk about ways to exercise those rights that it specified. They accepted that 'rights' could not always be demanded in the NHS and that they had to show understanding about the limited capabilities of a service under pressure.

When John Major first brought out this Patient's Charter, he wanted you to feel that you had some rights. But in actual fact, people pay National Insurance and when they go into hospital, obviously, they do think that, you know, they have a right to these things. But at the same time, I think it's asking

> *rather a lot of a service that is – well, let's face it the demands that are made on it now, they never expected this in a million years.*
>
> Chesterfield

While accepting that they should have 'rights' in the NHS, there was a feeling that perhaps these should best be considered as 'expectations'; this seemed a more helpful definition, and also a more realistic approach. 'Rights' were something that could be demanded, whereas expectations suggested working in harmony towards a set of fundamental principles. However, patients still welcomed a framework which set out what they could reasonably expect from the NHS.

> *A lot of people think they're entitled to so many things and that's not what it's all about. What they're trying to do is make things easier for us and explain more to us when we go in hospital. So I think 'expectations' would be a much better word, and it would say an awful lot for you if you were going into hospital and would expect to be told what is going to happen, and you would expect to receive a courtesy, and you would expect to return a courtesy and show appreciation for what you've had done. I think that would be an awful lot better – expectations.*
>
> Chesterfield

Staff perspectives

Staff wanted the aim of the new charter to be stated clearly.

> *To start with one has really to identify the aim of the Charter – very important to set out what you want from the new charter, and it's very easy then to identify the standards. So the first question is, do we need really to tell patients what [is] expected, do we need to raise their expectations, do we need to improve performance? All these need to be addressed first and then very easily you will pull out the standards by talking to professionals.*
>
> Clinicians

Staff also had a range of opinions about the Charter: should it establish minimum standards for service provision or should it set goals and aspirations for the service? Some felt that setting baseline standards would provide a challenge to encourage better quality services. The key points mentioned in favour of and against a minimum standards versus aspirational model for the

Charter are summarised in Chart 3. Some staff also suggested that a hybrid of the two might provide a baseline for what patients can expect now as well as specific targets for the future.

Chart 3 Views about a minimum standards versus an aspirational model

Minimum standards	**Aspirational standards**
In favour of minimum standards:	*In favour of aspirational standards:*
• should establish the basics so everyone knows the services they are entitled to	• should be about what the NHS is working towards rather than rights, which cannot always be met
Against minimum standards:	• should be forward looking, but realistic
• 'drags' the service down to the lowest common denominator and is soul-destroying for staff because it is not progressive	• should be linked to strategic thinking about the status of the NHS in 5–10 years and standards to meet that projection
• encourages only negative feedback about the service	

Areas to be covered in the Charter

As patients in the focus groups knew little about the content of the present Charter, they were asked to create a list of issues that were important to them. The same issues cropped up in each group, suggesting that there are fundamental areas which service users find significant. Chart 4 presents an overview (see page 107).

Equity in access to and quality of services

First, equity is the key requirement for patients: they wanted fair and equal access to the service for all patients, regardless of ability to pay. They also wanted equity in the quality of NHS services.

Patients did not feel that equity prevailed in either sense at the moment. They were concerned that private health care was draining NHS resources and that patients who could afford, would receive better services and faster access to them. They also felt there were unfair variations in the quality of health care provision, across health authority boundaries and across different sub-groups of the population. It was said that older people fare less well than others in the NHS.

As long as you have got private health it will never be [equitable]. Someone can go along and jump the queue because they have got £20,000 or whatever it is for a kidney operation, while the man or woman next door is unemployed and can't get on the waiting list. You are never going to have equality in the health service until you ban private health. And it really annoys me because, if you have got money, you can jump that queue and get that service with the exact same nurses, the same operating theatre, the same consultant.

Banbury

Giving priority to patients according to clinical need was seen as the fair thing to do. Patients said they would be willing to accept longer delays for treatment if reassured that clinical urgency was the criterion for queuing. They also liked the idea of introducing a formal mechanism that would enable patients to give their views on the way priorities are selected for services in the NHS. This should be discussed more openly.

I would have been quite happy to have sat back and waited a little bit longer, even if it had been threatening my life, if someone in a terrible condition was having to wait in a queue for me – I would have hated that.

Chesterfield

Better access to information

Information was important to patients in many ways. First, having more information was a first step towards more choice and participating more actively in their own health care. They would like more information about treatment alternatives, the qualifications of doctors to whom they have been referred or general practitioners with whom they might register, and the range of services available in their area.

Second, information enabled patients to feel more in control of their situation and helped them deal more effectively and have fewer anxieties about it. Specifically, they wanted information about issues such as their condition or treatment and what would happen next regarding them, why there were problems with the service or their treatment and the implications for them as patients, and how long they could expect to wait and why.

It is nice to know why you are kept waiting. It stops you getting stressed out [about] why you are waiting if someone comes and says it's because someone has collapsed.

Banbury

Lastly, without proper access to information, patients felt that they could not exercise their rights as service users. They needed to know what they were entitled to, what was available to them, how they could access the services and where they could get more help or information if required.

If you had a charter that educated people to their rights in the health service, then they would be able to push the health service to deliver a better service for them.

Walthamstow

The manner in which patients were given information was also important. They wanted things clearly explained to them and to be able to ask questions. They also wanted certain types of information published and freely available, such as lists of services offered by general practitioners and lists of doctors' qualifications, specialists as well as general practitioners.

A good standard of clinical treatment

Patients said there were specific components of good clinical care which they would expect as a matter of course, such as correct diagnosis and referral to specialists when necessary. However, many felt that doctors were the 'experts' and it was difficult therefore to make any assessment of their work. Instead of making judgements on doctors themselves, patients needed to trust them and have faith that the system would monitor the standards of doctors on their behalf. Though reassured by qualifications and certificates, they also wanted to know that a system existed for continuously monitoring doctors' competence and that their skills were kept updated.

You'd want some sort of supervisory or monitoring system for the professionals. The old story that the medical profession buries its mistakes is very real and very poignant and I'm sure we can all point to people we know or members of our family who have gone that way. There ought to be a way that incompetent, inefficient and grossly negligent medical practitioners should be got rid of.

Walthamstow

Positive interaction with staff

From their interactions with NHS staff, both positive and negative, patients formed a series of principles. First, they asked for respect and wished to be treated as a person, not a number or a medical condition. They felt that doctors sometimes spoke patronisingly to them or, worse, talked about them to medical students or colleagues as if they were not there.

> *I think this business about the right to know ties in with one doctor talking to another doctor across you as if you're not there. You feel like saying, 'I'm the patient, I'm the one that you're referring to, I'm the one. Could you include me in the conversation?' That's another right that we need.*
>
> Walthamstow

Patients also wanted to be listened to by doctors and taken seriously. There were stories of people being told it 'was all in their head' and 'brushed off', which left them feel dissatisfied, unable to find alternative help and reluctant to return to the doctor to press their point or ask for further assistance. In some cases, patients felt doctors preferred to write a quick prescription and seemed to prefer this to listening.

They were aware, too, that NHS staff are under pressure to attend to patients quickly and this made them feel guilty about taking up time. They would like to ask questions of staff until they fully understand their condition and greatly appreciate compassion, kindness and sympathy, but feel this is sometimes asking too much.

> *The doctor spent 20 minutes of his time, which I felt very guilty about, telling me exactly what was going on in my throat. Which is brilliant. I walked away and I know exactly [what's wrong]. I was very impressed by him doing this for me. But the fact that I felt quite guilty sitting there and taking up the man's time. It's down to the fact that there aren't a lot of doctors in there. I don't want to monopolise anybody's time because I realise that there aren't a lot of doctors but there are a lot of people to see.*
>
> Banbury

Assurance of privacy and confidentiality

Patients also wanted more privacy when being examined and when discussing their situation with doctors. Recent experiences were mentioned which involved patients being asked for personal information in front of other people, of patients being on wards where the bed curtains were so thin that others could see through them, and being embarrassed by strangers entering the room while receiving treatment.

> *I was astounded to see men down the other side of the ward. And I said to this lady, 'There's a man over there', and she said, 'Yes, it's ghastly.' She said, 'I have to be so careful getting in and out of bed, it's so embarrassing ...' and she said, 'He's none too particular with himself. It's all very embarrassing ...' Well, I wouldn't have liked that. The examinations are very personal and although they draw the curtains, they never quite draw them, do they? I mean just to draw the curtain and then talk about it, everybody in the ward hearing.*
>
> Manchester

More choice

One reason why patients required more information was to enable them to make more informed choices. They were sometimes unclear about the alternatives available and felt that they must simply take whatever was offered to them. Examples of this included the belief that they must take whatever GP would accept them (regardless of factors such as quality of reputation with local residents or their gender), that they could not change consultants, and that they could not refuse to be place in a mixed-sex hospital ward. The prevailing view was that people must be grateful for whatever they could get from the NHS.

This feeling was partly reinforced by the perception that the NHS works with over-stretched resources and alternative choices are unavailable. This, in turn, means that the patient is not offered more choices because he or she seldom asks for them. They are sometimes pleasantly surprised to find that alternatives do exist which they did not know about. For example, the mother of a young child was very pleased to discover that health visitors were available to give advice and support. She learned this from a friend rather than her GP because she was too concerned about taking up the GP's time to enquire.

When patients were unhappy with NHS services, they felt that they had to cope with what was on offer or turn to private health care if they could afford it.

It's not like we can vote with our feet. AJ's Roadside Café gives you a monitoring form where they say: 'Our aim is to serve you'. What did you feel about our service? And you fill that in and you leave it. If you don't like the service, you don't ever use AJ's again. If you live [in this area] where do you go? We can't vote with our feet as I've tried, you cannot move across these boundaries we've got. We're landed with this health authority, with this level of service, and all we can do is shift around somewhere that I wouldn't choose as an ideal thing. We can't vote with our feet, so what can we do?

Walthamstow

Patients' responsibilities

The question of whether patients have responsibilities themselves was a subject on which they had conflicting views. A minority felt that it was inappropriate to enshrine patients' responsibilities in the Charter. They believed it was unreasonable to specify responsibilities as this might prevent some people from using NHS services. It was also felt to be patronising with the implicit suggestion that people did not know how to behave properly.

Those who felt that patients' responsibilities should be included in the Charter suggested three approaches to consider: Patients should: (1) make appropriate use of services; (2) behave in a civil way to staff and try to co-operate in their own health care; and (3) keep paying their taxes to fund the service. A detailed list of responsibilities under these headings appears in Chart 5.

Patients find already that such responsibilities are difficult to comply with. It can be hard to get through to the GP's surgery to cancel appointments, and how do you define 'appropriate use of services'? Specific examples raised were:

- appropriate use of A&E departments, especially:
  - if patients need help at a time when their GP's surgery is closed
  - if they are unable to get an appointment with their GP for a considerable length of time (e.g. 2–3 weeks)

- appropriate occasions on which to request a home visit from their GP, especially –
  - immediately following discharge from hospital when they may feel unable to get to the GP
  - when patients are unsure about the severity of the illness and the GP's surgery is closed
  - when they do not feel well enough to get to the surgery.

Chart 4 Patients' priorities for the Charter

Patients felt they had a right to or could expect:

- **Equality in access to and quality of services**
- **Comprehensible information about:**
  - services available to them
  - their own health and treatment options
  - the nature of their treatment and what will happen next (and when)
  - reasons for service delays or long waits or problems with health care
  - how people are given priority for treatment and on what basis
  - general practitioners in their area and their qualifications
  - the qualifications of specialists to whom they may be referred

- **Positive interaction with NHS staff, including:**
  - being listened to and 'taken seriously'
  - being respected and treated courteously
  - receiving an apology for mistakes
  - being treated as a person, not a medical condition
  - being talked to, not about, as when staff are discussing their case with others
  - being treated as an adult and not patronised
  - being treated supportively and sympathetically
  - not being made to feel guilty or 'difficult' for seeking help or taking up time

- **A good standard of clinical treatment, specifically:**
  - a correct diagnosis
  - competent and appropriate treatment and medical advice
  - treatment and care at an appropriate pace, not hurried
  - prompt referrals to specialists where necessary
  - consistent care from staff familiar with the patient's history

- **Improved access to the NHS, particularly:**
  - quicker access to general practitioners
  - more flexible hours for general practitioners
  - shorter waits for outpatient appointments
  - shorter waiting in A&E departments
  - fewer cancellations of operations on the appointed day

- **Assurance of privacy and confidentiality, specifically:**
  - respect of confidentiality from all staff responsible for patient care
  - patients should be asked personal questions only in private
  - patients should be able to discuss their case privately with their doctor
  - access to patients' notes should be restricted to NHS staff only
  - patients should be examined in properly private conditions

- **More choice, in terms of:**
  - the consultant they are referred to
  - the general practitioners with whom they may register
  - referrals to alternative practitioners
  - treatment in a mixed-sex hospital ward or not
  - the gender of their doctor

Because of uncertainty about the use of services, patients were worried that they may be misusing them, that they would upset the doctor, that they would take up too much of the doctor's time, an so on. Their initial approach was to the GP and if the GP was unavailable or unresponsive, they tended to look elsewhere, usually to the A&E department.

It became clear patients needed to know how to use services appropriately and required help in doing so. This may simply mean more responsive staff on switchboards when patients call to cancel appointments, or it may necessitate more fundamental changes, such as provision of better sources of information and advice.

Chart 5 Patients' views about their responsibilities

Patients recognised their responsibility to:

- **Use services appropriately, by:**
  - keeping appointments or making reasonable attempts to cancel them
  - turning up to appointments on time
  - not wasting doctors' time or calling out ambulances unnecessarily, etc.
- **Behave appropriately as a patient, by:**
  - being civil and polite to NHS staff
  - listening to and trying to follow advice offered
  - trying to be positive and appreciative of help received
  - trying to be co-operative with staff who are trying to help
- **Pay their taxes to help finance the NHS**

Staff views about areas to be covered in the Charter

Staff were, of course, already familiar with the Charter, and were better able to make suggestions as to how it might be revised. A summary of appears in Chart 6.

Clinical quality

Staff wanted more emphasis on monitoring service quality and those aspects of it which were high among the priorities of clinicians or which they felt were important to patients. They rejected standards that interfere with clinical decisions, but felt there were mechanisms that could measure quality more appropriately. They felt the Charter could bring attention to the quality of health care and clinical outcomes for patients.

Service responsiveness

GPs noted that patients are sometimes allowed to drift through the system without any communication or comprehension of what to anticipate. They wanted something in the Charter about regular communication with patients to prove that their situation was being actively addressed. This also reflects a concern by staff that patients with chronic conditions or continuous care receive insufficient attention in the current Charter. One suggestion made was that the Charter should require clear care plans for patients.

Information

NHS staff agreed with patients that more information should given to them. Staff emphasised, however, that the Charter should be realistic to avoid falsely raising patients' expectations. They highlighted the need to tell patients of choices available in their local area.

Staff were keen to provide information to help patients understand more about the clinical performance of NHS facilities in their area which may also guide them to make more informed choices about doctors. Patients wanted this information too, but felt that they had to trust NHS quality assurance systems to ensure that a clinician can perform to a high standard. Some patients felt confident about their ability to use this information to choose their own doctor, while others felt that such decisions were best left to 'experts', such as GPs or other doctors. It would appear that if such information were made available to patients, they would benefit from support in interpreting and using it effectively.

Neglected groups

Consistent with the view that the current Charter concerns itself with particular service areas such as acute care, some staff felt that more emphasis should be placed on those who have been marginalised or neglected under the current arrangements. Specific groups mentioned were mental health service users for whom the current Charter has limited relevance, patients with chronic, continuing needs, and carers whose rights to information and support are not currently featured.

Respect and dignity

Staff wanted to increase the emphasis on respect and dignity to include patients and staff alike. This was seen as one way to balance the Charter and make it less biased towards patients. In addition, some felt there should be clearer statements about appropriate behaviour, including what patients and staff could expect in their relationships with one another.

There was a general feeling that patients judge service quality by their relationships with staff and they suggested that the new Charter should therefore focus more on improving the quality of this interaction and encourage the development of clinical practices which give patients more respect and dignity. Specifically, staff were already aware that privacy is sometimes lacking and that services may not be as culturally sensitive as they should be. They felt that improvements should be encouraged in these areas.

Patients' responsibilities

Lastly, as this is a charter that applies to both patients and staff, managers and clinicians wanted patients' own responsibilities to be more explicit. They felt that patients needed a clear sense of what they could realistically expect from the service.

They also want to see improved standards of patient behaviour, both in their relationships with members of staff and the way they use the services provided. Staff felt that the responsibility of patients to use the services appropriately should be highlighted and to support this, information about services should be collected and made widely available. For example, there was a suggestion that '*did not attend*' data should be published locally and nationally along with the cost to the NHS of this behaviour as a way to make patients more aware of their responsibilities and the repercussions if they fail to use services properly.

It should be recalled, however, that patients themselves were unsure about the precise definition of 'appropriate use of services' (e.g. unable to get through on the switchboard to cancel an appointment) and staff said they did not want patients afraid to use services if there was genuine need, a quality that is sometimes difficult to define. Some clinicians pointed out that this may be an area where the specific roles of primary and acute care need further consideration before advice about using them can be given to patients.

Chart 6 Staff priorities for the Charter

Staff wanted to change the emphasis and coverage of the Charter to include:

- **Clinical quality, including:**
  - clinical outcomes
  - clinical audit
  - emphasis on treatment according to clinical need

- **Service responsiveness, particularly:**
  - clearer care plans so that patients know and understand what to anticipate
  - better communication with patients
  - faster communication with patients
  - clearer, more honest explanations in response to complaints

- **Provision of information to patients on:**
  - clinical performance (linked to performance indicators)
  - clinical outcomes and morbidity
  - choices available to them, including alternative services
  - the full range of services available to them

- **Neglected groups:**
  - patients with ongoing needs from the NHS because of chronic conditions
  - carers and their entitlement to support and information
  - greater Charter relevance to mental health patients

- **Respect and dignity, including:**
  - applicability to both staff and patients
  - clearer statements on how to treat people
  - more emphasis on the quality of interaction with patients

- **Patients' responsibilities, including:**
  - more clarity about what people can reasonably expect from the service
  - more emphasis on appropriate behaviour with staff
  - not wasting NHS resources by inappropriate use of services
  - clarify the implications of inappropriate usage to patients

Comparison of staff priorities for the Charter (Chart 6) with those of patients (Chart 4) reveals considerable areas of common ground, though there are differences of emphasis which may require further negotiation. Key areas of agreement were:

- provision of more information to patients, including explanations of the choices available to them
- quality of interaction between patients and staff

- more emphasis on respect and dignity (which is linked to, though perhaps does not entirely incorporate, patients' priorities for privacy and confidentiality)
- more emphasis on using the Charter as a quality assurance tool focusing on clinical outcomes and clinical excellence
- the principle of treatment according to clinical need as the basic premise for the allocation of services
- more service commitment to keep patients better informed.

There were also differences between what patients and NHS staff wanted to include in the new Charter. Staff felt that the current drive for reduced waiting times had gone far enough, but patients wished it could go further. Although patients were not usually aware of the specific waiting times mentioned in the current Charter, their recent experiences with NHS services led them to hope that they would be further reduced. Some clinicians, particularly general practitioners, said that waiting times for outpatient appointments should be reduced and patients agreed with them on this. Patients also felt that waiting times to see GPs themselves should be reduced. Seeing a GP, they pointed out, is made more difficult because surgeries are usually open only during working hours. Patients wanted primary care services made more flexible and responsive to their needs. Some patients had also experienced cancellations of operations on the appointed day and mentioned the anxiety and stress this had caused them. They felt it should be possible to give patients proper advance notification of cancellations and wanted this to be included in the Charter.

Another area of disagreement between patients and staff was the issue of choice. Staff felt that provision of information was generally the key to giving patients more choice. While certainly important, patients desired more information about the services and alternatives available to them, they also wanted greater choice over such issues as which doctor they could be referred to or which GP to register with. This was partly about distribution of resources as patients are aware that some health authorities offer more choices than others and they wanted the same range of choices available throughout the system; staff, however, felt that this was unrealistic, and that patients should be informed only of those choices which are available locally.

Privacy and confidentiality were important to patients, particularly in hospitals. This became more of an issue for people in mixed-sex wards. This feeling of lack of privacy and respect gave rise to many comments which hinted at a sense of dehumanisation. Images used by patients were that people had been treated like cattle or sheep.

Staff also felt that privacy and dignity should receive greater emphasis, but this was not an issue which they carried through to their Charter revision. However, they pointed out that as these standards are difficult to measure statistically, they are not included in the monitoring exercises and therefore receive less attention than those that can. They agreed that they should be emphasised more in a new charter.

Staff suggestions for revising charter standards

There were basic principles to follow, staff felt, when establishing new standards or revising the existing ones and Chart 7 presents a summary of the suggestions. Once the nature and format of the revised Charter has been agreed upon, the specific standards must be devised in consultation with professionals from each of the services involved, and only then will it be possible to establish the form that standards themselves will take.

Views about the ethos and format of a revised charter

There were two issues which staff felt were fundamental to any discussion about the format that the Charter should take:

- should it be national or local?
- should it be aspirational or merely establish minimum standards?

Minimum standards model

The choice appears to lie between a charter that sets basic standards to which everyone knows they are entitled and a charter which aspires to principles and targets which will encourage service improvement without establishing patients' basic rights. Put simply, this is a bill of rights for patients on one hand and a policy manifesto of goals and intentions on the other.

Staff and patients both pointed out that there appear to be no sanctions built into the current Charter which can be implemented if either side fails to meet standards. This needs to be considered if a 'minimum rights' model is adopted, though there are obvious difficulties: how, for instance, could patients be sanctioned if they fail to meet their responsibilities as service users.

A local or national charter framework?

Staff felt that standards would be more realistic if they took into account the resources, current provision and context within local areas: national standards highlighted the differences between service areas, but this was not always helpful as they presented little challenge in some areas but in other areas standards could never realistically be achieved within the constraints of local resources and circumstances. Staff therefore suggested that the revised Charter might involve a national framework combined with locally set standards which were relevant to local circumstances.

Specific problems here concerned the need for careful regulation to ensure that local standards did not become too divorced from standards which were nationally acceptable. There was also a risk this might conflict with the universal principle of equity which patients felt was important. To establish local

Chart 7 Principles for a new charter

- **Always leave enough flexibility in standards to cater for meeting clinical needs first**
  - avoid the use of 'blanket statements' which restrict ability to use professional discretion
  - avoid creating conflicts between existing systems of priority (e.g. national triage priorities) and Charter priorities
- **Consider the larger NHS picture in creating standards**
  - create standards which address the movement of patients from one part of the system to another, giving equal consideration to what happens in each part of the system
- **Create standards which emphasise clinical outcome and performance**
  - as measured objectively by clinical audit
  - as measured subjectively by patient satisfaction
- **Create and monitor 'softer' standards to encourage improvement in the quality of patients' experiences. Specific issues might include:**
  - cultural sensitivity
  - privacy and dignity
  - treatment contexts and environments
  - quality of interaction between staff and patients
- **Make standards challenging to encourage improvement but realistic to avoid demoralisation**
  - standards should not be set at a level which raises patients' expectations unrealistically
  - meaningful and realistic standards must vary across service areas and areas of the country
  - localised standards may be more realistic as they will reflect the nature of local services and resources

standards in this way was to acknowledge that service users cannot expect an equal standard of services. If it is to promote equity, the Charter would need to be based on standards which can be reached across the service as a whole, though some areas would clearly exceed the targets. One alternative is for a local element of the Charter that establishes aspirational standards beyond a national minimum which is realistic but also challenging at a local level.

The ethos of a new charter

Staff mentioned the importance of adopting a positive tone in the new charter. They suggested this could be achieved by:

- emphasising a more co-operative relationship, or partnership, between staff and patients
- inviting positive as well as negative feedback from patients on their experiences with NHS services and encouraging better communication between patients and staff
- adopting language which reinforces the message of co-operation rather than establishing an adversarial tone
- presenting the notion of equal rights and responsibilities of both patients and staff.

A more co-operative relationship

Staff commonly felt that the message of the new Charter should be one of partnership – patients and staff working together to improve the service. They described this variously as a stronger 'stakeholder' philosophy in the NHS, as promoting a greater sense of community spirit with less emphasis on individualism, and as presenting the Charter as a 'covenant' rather than a 'contract'.

Inviting more positive and constructive communication

Staff felt the ethos of the Charter should deliberately encourage a broad spectrum of patient response, not just complaints. They hoped a system could be introduced at a local level to invite more collaboration from patients.

Adopting language which encourages co-operation

There was a commonly held view among staff that the language of the current Charter is adversarial. Many felt that it was biased against them, rather than a positive statement to assist both service users and providers. They wanted a new Charter that expressed a more positive attitude equally towards patients and staff.

Presenting rights and responsibilities as equally balanced

Staff also said that patient responsibilities virtually ignored the current Charter, while patient rights were over-emphasised. They felt that the new charter should exhibit a more balanced approach.

Rights versus expectations

A final point made by staff involved the current distinction between 'rights' and 'expectations'. Generally, staff did not feel that this was useful because patients could not distinguish between them in practice. Patients expected services described in the Charter irrespective of 'rights' or 'expectations', and staff still had to cope with their dissatisfaction if their wishes were not met.

There were differences of opinion on how to resolve this issue. Some felt that nothing should be included in the Charter which is not a 'right' so that patients have no unrealistic expectations of the service. Others pointed out that emphasising rights may encourage a combative desire for sanctions when it was felt they have not been met.

Managing and implementing a new charter

This section draws on lessons managers and clinicians feel have been learned in managing the current Charter and deals with three key areas they identified as important: overall management issues; the monitoring of Charter standards; and other initiatives which could help meet Charter objectives. Chart 8 summarises the points raised.

A positive and constructive approach

A key theme here was that a new charter should represent a more positive attempt to address service quality. It was important to manage the Charter in a more positive way and avoid the culture of blame which seems to accompany the present one. This might entail removing some of the pressure to achieve standards and placing more emphasis instead on using the monitoring of standards and the information thus obtained as a learning experience. Staff felt it was clearly important to improve service quality rather than find someone to blame when not up to standard.

There were staff who said it would help if the government publicly acknowledged the generally high quality of services provided by the NHS. A supportive tone from policy-makers as well as a genuine commitment to the

Charter, built on by successive governments, was seen as one means by which staff themselves might feel happier with it.

Resource implications

Staff said that some improvements *will* require more resources and that if policy-makers are genuinely committed to them then money should be allocated to make them happen.

Furthermore, some staff believed that money was being wasted on the Charter at the moment. They felt savings could be made if money were not spent needlessly on glossy brochures advertising the Charter and wanted an end to the practice of using expensive and scarce clinical staff to carry out the monitoring of standards. It was also pointed out that resources should not be spent monitoring standards which are irrelevant to some services: if the standards do not apply in a particular service area, they should be exempt from monitoring.

Encourage commitment

The current Charter is thought to be superficial or irrelevant to issues which are important to NHS professionals and patients. To give it substance, it should contribute positively to organisational learning. In order to do this, it must provide a sound basis for gathering useful information and be able to feed that information back into service development. Better feedback mechanisms between monitoring and service planning, improved responses from patients, and clinical audits rather than narrow monitoring were all suggested as ways to make the Charter more valuable to staff. Additionally, it should be linked more fundamentally into existing and planned initiatives to improve service quality so that it becomes an essential focus for that quality.

> *If we have to measure something then let's measure something meaningful. If people are really interested in what goes on in a hospital, then I think it's back to the drawing board and we look at everything that goes on in there. How else can you measure it? It might be something [like] once a year, when you have a team of inspectors who go in and do some kind of audit.*
>
> Managers

Set more meaningful targets

Staff suggested that the standards themselves should also be revised to ensure that they really address service quality and do so in a realistic way. This should draw on existing knowledge and research into what works best and also involve greater collaboration with those responsible for implementing them. Imposition of standards by people who seem not to understand the service was regarded as a major problem with the current charter, and is responsible for the lack of commitment by staff. Consultation, they felt, was important in gaining support for the revised charter.

> *One positive thing is that it's proved that setting standards without going back to the actual people who are going to implement them initially and consulting them is going to be a failure. It's time now really to be looking at some evidence, if we can get some, or at least talk to the people who are going to carry on this standard.*
>
> Clinicians

Find more constructive ways of addressing complaints

The current methods for dealing with complaints from patients were regarded as bureaucratic and time-consuming, as well as potentially daunting for the patients themselves. Staff believe that time, resources and anguish could be saved by attempting, where possible, to address these problems as they arise rather than wait for them to be formalised in writing. Although this is not always feasible, staff accept that what patients often really need is to be listened to and to feel that someone has understood their problem and perhaps apologised. More training in dealing effectively with complaints was one suggestion. Additionally, staff felt there should be more encouragement from managers to learn from complaints rather than view them as threatening and adversarial.

Lastly, there were staff who felt that NHS letters about complaints tend to be written more to 'conceal' the organisation's difficulties rather than to explain them honestly to patients. Some believed that being open with patients about the real problems experienced by the health service would help them understand how it actually works.

> *We've got a complaints officer and she does the job well, but I think it's basically down to every individual to take responsibility at whatever level and whatever sort of interaction we have with the patient. And I think we need to get this across to people. It's our responsibility, day-on-day, minute-on-minute. Instead of just brushing the patient off, you actually settle the complaint there and then, and I think that's the way forward.*
>
> Managers

A holistic view of the service

Some staff felt that primary care received too little attention in the Charter. They said that primary care staff had escaped the thrust of the Charter initiative, unlike those who work in acute trusts, despite the fact that primary care staff are the gatekeepers to acute care and are responsible for patients both before and after they receive hospital treatment. In order to reinforce the holistic message of the Charter as a total quality movement within the NHS, primary care staff need encouragement to become more actively involved in the Charter initiative.

> *It's very different from our relationship with the GPs, because while they have some responsibility for, they have no accountability to it. The trust and the health authority both have an accountability for it and you work together on it. Once you start working with someone who has a responsibility but no accountability, then it's a very different sort of relationship. We're seen as being bureaucratic and implementing what the Government says without thinking about its relevance. We have to implement it, but the GPs don't. And I think that's something that needs to be taken into account particularly as they're responsible for the contracts, [but] they're not interested in anything around the Patient's Charter being in the contract.*
>
> Managers

Better guidance on inconsistencies

Other difficulties experienced with the current Charter are the inconsistencies between standards to be met in the main national Charter and those in specialist charters such as the one for mental health services. Staff wanted the Charters scrutinised for such inconsistencies or, alternatively, better guidance on which set of standards they should be seeking to achieve.

> *There are some conflicts between some of the Charters as well – I mean the Mental Health Charter and the national Patient's Charter. We have a problem because it says within the Mental Health Charter that if you're referred to a specialist mental health service, you should be seen within four weeks. In the national Charter, its says you can expect to be seen within four hours if you're an urgent patient, two days if you're non-urgent, but within the Mental Health, it's four weeks. Now I did ring the Patient's Charter office and ask them which standard we were supposed to go by and they said, whichever you want! What kind of guidance is that? If they suddenly decided*

to monitor that as a national standard who is going to know which one should be abided by?

Managers

Transition to the new Charter

Many people agreed that staff would take the Charter more seriously if they felt that policy-makers themselves were taking it seriously and actively trying to use to improve services. They felt that if it had any lasting value, it was worth taking time to consult, to implement changes where necessary, and to start afresh with a new charter. They also wanted the monitoring of existing standards to be suspended during this transitional period so that staff were not pressured to meet the old standards while trying to set up more appropriate systems for the new ones.

One of the lessons from the last one is that trying to make the service jump is very difficult because it's too big, it's too cumbersome. We ought to give the new Charter plenty of time to get in, plenty of time for staff to be trained and to understand it so that instead of having it in place within the next six months, it will be 18 months or two years. And by that date, we will have trained people appropriately to do this sort of thing, rather than the very rapid response that's been expected in previous initiatives.

Managers

Chart 8 Suggestions for managing the Charter

- **A positive and constructive approach**
  - stop allocating blame and make it a learning experience
  - the Government should publicly acknowledge the strengths of the NHS, be supportive and encourage a follow-through on the Charter from one government to the next
- **Consider resource issues more carefully**
  - resources should be commensurate with targets set
  - do not waste money on : glossy brochures, diverting expensive clinical resources to monitoring the Charter; measuring 'meaningless' outcomes
- **Encourage commitment**
  - establish better feedback loops to learn from monitoring (that is, more emphasis on why problems have occurred and how they can be rectified)
  - incorporate patients' views into feedback and create better understanding between patients and staff

cont.

- make clinical audits and disseminate best practice, thereby learning from the successes of other areas
- link the Charter into broader quality initiatives so that it is part of, and supported by, a wider programme of change

- **Set more meaningful targets**
  - incorporate patients' views into the setting of the next standards to ensure they are what patients want
  - seek evidence of what works best before setting standards, in keeping with broader move towards evidence-based practice in the NHS
  - consult the people who will implement the standards to ensure they are realistic

- **Find more constructive ways of addressing patients' complaints**
  - ensure greater emphasis on listening to patients
  - make more attempts to address complaints as they arise rather than waiting for formal complaints
  - encourage an environment where staff can be less defensive about complaints and use them constructively for service improvement
  - be more honest and less bureaucratic in answering patients' complaints

- **Take a more holistic view of the service**
  - contact between GPs as purchasers and hospitals as providers tends to deal mainly with quantity instead of quality, GPs should be encouraged to consider the issue of quality within the NHS
  - primary services must be included in the overall effort to improve quality and ensure smoother transitions for patients

- **Better guidance on inconsistencies**
  - iron out inconsistencies between charters or make clearer which charter standards should take precedence
  - consider how standards merge and overlap across service areas and be sure that staff are not uncertain about action to take

- **Transition to the new Charter**
  - allow enough time to implement the new Charter effectively
  - turn off the monitoring and start again with the new system
  - do not make staff feel they are being scrutinised while moving to a new system

Suggestions for monitoring

Suggestions for improving the monitoring of Charter standards related to four main areas:

- improving and expanding the methodological tools available for measuring Charter standards
- improving the quality of the data collected
- monitoring both the rights and responsibilities associated with the Charter
- spreading the load for monitoring by getting others involved

A summary of the key suggestions made by staff is provided in Chart 9.

Improving and expanding the methodological tools for monitoring

Although staff felt that the current methods were unable to measure what were described as 'softer standards' (privacy and dignity), they disagreed about how this could be resolved. There were different views as to whether something could be 'measured' without quantification and statistical output. A common refrain, however, was that more use should be made of qualitative measures to attempt deeper understanding of service quality than can be obtained through statistical indicators. While this could provide useful data on aspects of the Charter that seem currently 'unmeasurable', because they are not quantifiable, this might require more guidance and support than statistical monitoring.

> *There are other ways to measure things without using a figure measurement, but like most areas of research and anything else, unless it's a figure, people aren't as comfortable with it. But there are now proven ways of measuring something qualitatively, and we need to get that knowledge into the service to enable people to see how it can actually be measured robustly and qualitatively. It can be done.*
>
> Managers

Staff also suggested that clinical audits should be introduced, as a means of providing deeper understanding of service quality. Staff felt it was important, however, to consult clinicians on how this should best be done.

> *I think what is more useful in Patient's Charter monitoring would be something like the development of the creditation system as with the Ambulance Service, or, better still, use of clinical audit and maybe making the results of it more widely known. Because what's important is measuring what*

we do against what is known about what is good. So if the Patient's Charter monitoring continues we need to develop something more sophisticated that can tell patients real things about the ability of the institution they're involved in to deliver to them clinical care as well as the soft stuff which, at the moment, we don't measure. I think CHCs and user groups and that whole approach is probably the best way of moving forward on this one.

Managers

Improve the reliability of the data obtained

Staff had several suggestions about how to make data more reliable and comparable. These included the need for more effective information technology resources to help with monitoring, and relieving the pressures on clinical staff who have to monitor charter standards while also dealing with their other clinical duties.

In terms of monitoring, there is no control about how people do things, and then when you have league tables, they are not always comparing like with like. If we're going to be monitoring, we have to be meaningful in some way.

Managers

Eliminating the blame syndrome from the Charter and creating clear feedback loops from monitoring into service improvements may also relieve the pressure on staff to 'fudge' the results of monitoring exercises.

Collaborate on monitoring

Staff felt that greater collaboration on monitoring would shift the burden off acute care staff who are currently responsible for it: this diverts their resources from clinical duties and puts extra pressure on them so that spreading the load among various other 'stakeholders' in the NHS would obviously be a great help.

Second, the inclusion of more stakeholders in monitoring would reinforce the notion of partnership and broaden the commitment to the Charter by helping others to see how they can contribute more effectively to positive outcomes. Greater response from patients who could provide feedback, and getting community health councils to help with monitoring were suggested as ways of encouraging outside collaboration. Primary care staff are also in a unique position to conduct monitoring as they see more clearly the transitions out of acute care and are better placed to monitor issues such as appropriate follow-up after hospital discharge. Also highlighted was the importance of involving primary care specialists more actively in improving service quality across the NHS.

> *What we've started in our health authority is working with local general practices to monitor the services and trusts so what actually comes back to the practice after an outpatient appointment is, the discharge letters, all that sort of thing. That saves the trusts all the effort of doing it themselves and I think it's far more meaningful, but constantly pushing at trusts to produce yet more and more monitoring data takes them further and further away from clinical practice [and that] is a worry to me.*
>
> Managers

Collect and publish statistics on patients' performance

To help create a more balanced Charter, focusing equally on the rights and responsibilities of both staff and patients, some staff suggested that information should be collected and published on how well patients themselves have been meeting their responsibilities to the NHS. This might make patients aware of the repercussions of their actions and help them to understand the implications of improper use of the NHS, both financially and with regard to waiting times.

Chart 9 Suggestions for improving the monitoring of charter standards

- Develop and introduce qualitative measures to monitor softer standards
- Use clinical audit to measure clinical outcomes and performance
- Improve the reliability and comparability of data collected
- Collect and publish statistics of patients' performance
- Encourage collaboration with patients, community health councils and primary care staff

Other types of support in meeting charter standards

To become more meaningful and act as more than just a stand-alone document, staff suggested other initiatives which might support the Charter; where possible, patients' views have also been included in this section. They are:

- developing collaboration and a productive dialogue
- providing education and training

- providing advocacy
- integrating the Charter with the broader NHS culture and its ways of working

Collaboration and productive dialogue

Staff felt that the Charter needed responses from patients to aid the impetus for change. Although they welcomed more patient input, it was hard to pinpoint the most appropriate form this should take. Spreading news of innovations and successes in patient involvement might be one solution.

Patients welcomed the chance to involve themselves this way and felt that focus groups were a good opportunity to share their views and to understand more about what is happening in the NHS. They also generally wanted to have more say in the way services are delivered and felt that consultative exercises of this type would be a positive way of involving them in the health service.

> *People should be able to put forward, their ideas. Why don't you do this in the NHS? Or, why don't you do that? To have a place where you can go and say that is useful rather than actually pinpointing a doctor or a surgery as with complaints.*
>
> Banbury

Lastly, there was much discussion among staff of the need to be more honest about such issues as priority of services. They felt this was the only way that patients would begin to understand the limits on the service and develop more realistic expectations.

> *But the rationing and prioritising is where it's all falling down ... because the service is gradually being pruned in a lot of areas and giving people a charter that says you have a right to expect everything that you want, when we're cutting back, puts us obviously on a collision course. So maybe there has to be something in it that says you have to accept that it is necessary to prioritise in certain cases and you must accept that.*
>
> Managers

Patients were aware that services are being prioritised, but felt they had no say in how this occurs. There was a sense that doctors are currently 'playing God' and that discussions about the distribution of health care resources should also involve patients.

It's absolutely clear to me that if it's a public health authority, it is the public who should have the right to sit down with the people making the decisions, listen to what they're saying and at appropriate times, contribute. It's going to help me to feel more confident that I'm going to have the best possible treatment out of my local health authority.

Patients' focus group

Education and training

Both patients and staff agreed that more education and training for clinicians, managers and patients would be helpful. First, education for patients was viewed as one way to help them use the NHS and the Charter more effectively. Specific areas where NHS professionals and patients themselves suggested such training would be useful were:

- how to make appropriate use of services, when to use each part of the service, and what the alternatives were
- training in first aid and how to deal with accidents
- teaching about the Charter and how to exercise their rights more effectively.

I think something that ought to go into any new Charter is making clear to people what the mechanism is for obtaining non-emergency treatment and what is defined as emergency. Because to me as a patient a bang on the knee is an emergency because I'm in pain, but clinically it's not. So I think, somehow, that issue has got to be addressed. Everybody knows that people turn up in A&E inappropriately because the primary care services are not meeting their needs.

Clinicians

Everybody needs educating in this Charter. We have things on television like The Time and the Place where people can go to air their views, and a lot of people do watch these things. In doctors' surgeries nowadays, like in the Post Office, you get a TV screen and they sometimes play health programmes. Why not establish something like this, but on a grander scale? Have it filmed and let people sit and watch that in the surgery. And then, afterwards, if you would like to join something like this, if you would like to put your views across, then get in contact with this number or this address. Then people can start to find out about it at least.

Banbury

It was also suggested that NHS professionals themselves would benefit from training by:

- continuing professional development to ensure high quality clinical skills
- education and training in customer care to improve relationships between patients and staff as well as learning to deal more effectively with complaints
- training for nurses in areas now dealt with exclusively by doctors (e.g. requesting X-rays, prescribing drugs) as a way to reduce waiting times.

> *My GP goes on courses and when you ring up for an appointment, she'll say he's either on his holidays or he's on a course for such and such a thing. And you know that he's updating and I think that's a good thing. At least you know that he's on refresher courses and things all the time.*
>
> Patients

Advocacy

As well as education and training for patients in how to use services more appropriately, and how to exercise their rights under the terms of the Charter, it was also suggested that advocacy services could be provided to help them find their way through an already complicated system. Specifically, further help in making complaints and following them through could be useful, particularly as patients fear making complaints and especially so when coping with illness, disability or discomfort. Patients would also welcome an independent third party to whom they could address complaints or air their views.

> *I'd like to have somebody like an ombudsman that you could go to, not necessarily to complain, but to clarify things.*
>
> Patients

> *I work in mental health and particularly in those areas people always say, 'You're doing your best'. And in fact you are, but I think if patients aren't facilitated to express an opinion about those kinds of things [quality issues], we're never going to change them.*
>
> Managers

Integrating the Charter with the wider NHS culture

Lastly, professionals felt that to be most effective, the Charter should be linked to wider trends in health care and be consistent with other initiatives occurring in the NHS. Specific suggestions included using it as a focus for locality commissioning (though this perhaps presumes it will include a locally determined element) and developing standards from sound evidence in accordance with the trend towards evidence-based practice.

> *You could address national issues broadly, broadbrush, but the actual documents that are interesting from the point of view of patients need to be much more local. If you're going to have locality commissioning then, obviously, the document follows from your locality commissioning, doesn't it?*
>
> Clinicians

Appendix 5

Research methods

The literature review

A review of the literature on the Patient's Charter was conducted which drew on books and journal articles that included specific references to it. Databases used to identify titles and abstracts included King's Fund, Unicorn, HealthSTAR, Medline, DH-Data, CINAHL and Reuter's Textline. Selected articles were examined in detail in order to review literature on the Charter that was relevant to a range of NHS settings from a variety of academic, clinical and lay perspectives. Having initially examined a small number of local charters, it was decided not to include them in the literature review since they contained local standards and did not add to critical thinking about the idea or application of the Patient's Charter itself.

In-depth interviews with voluntary organisations, patients' groups and representatives of vulnerable groups

Eight interviews were conducted with voluntary organisations and patients' groups. In five instances, the interview was conducted with a senior person from the organisation. In two instances, (Association of Community Health Councils in England and Wales and the National Consumer Council), the interview involved a small number of people from within the organisation, and in one instance (Long-term Medical Conditions Alliance – LMCA), there was an opportunity to use a large meeting of some 30 people who formed part of the LMCA in order to have a lengthy discussion on the Patient's Charter.

The organisations were selected using the following criteria:

- national groups
- links to local groups or projects
- groups whose remit included health issues, from user and/or carer perspectives
- groups known to be interested in the areas covered by the Patient's Charter.

With the exception of the LMCA meeting, the interviews were semi-structured to allow opportunities to comment on the working of the Patient's Charter to date and views on possible future developments.

In-depth interviews with representatives of vulnerable groups

In-depth interviews were conducted with organisations or groups for whom access to the NHS or quality within the NHS might pose particular difficulties. We spoke to groups concerned with the following issues or areas:

- physical disability
- sensory disabilities (blindness and deafness)
- minority ethnic communities
- refugees
- HIV/AIDS
- homelessness.

With the exception of the multi-ethnic women's project, which was a group meeting with a number group of health advocates, the interviews were conducted by telephone.

Written evidence

A ten per cent structured sample of NHS organisations was selected from Binley's database (England only), and the King's Fund databases of GPs and voluntary organisations. The sample produced 11 health authorities, 8 ambulance trusts, 15 acute trusts, 8 acute and community trusts, 17 community and mental health trusts, 19 community health councils, 28 general practices, 58 voluntary organisations, 14 Royal Colleges/professional organisations, and 2 trade unions. A letter and a short questionnaire were sent to a named person (usually the chief executive or senior officer). After three weeks approximately 30 per cent had responded and this included a number of organisations who said they were unable to offer comments for specific reasons such as pressure of work. A follow-up letter was sent to those who had not replied. By the end of December, 85 completed questionnaires had been returned. A telephone follow-up in January 1998 produced 7 more questionnaires but only four of these arrived before the cut-off date.

The analysis of the written evidence is based on these 89 completed returns, which represents a response rate of 49 per cent. However, the overall response rate, including those organisations who contacted us to say why they did not respond, was 65 per cent. The commonest reasons for not responding were that the time for replies was too short or the pressure of work was too great.

Table 1 shows the numbers and types of organisations included in the analysis.

Table 1 Organisations included in the analysis of written evidence

Type of Organisation	*Sample*
Health authorities	9
Acute trusts	11
Acute and community trusts	7
Community and mental health trusts	15
Ambulance trusts	6
General practitioners	6
Community health councils	10
Voluntary organisations	16
Royal colleges and professional organisations	9
Trade unions	0
TOTAL	**89**

Table 2 shows the overall response rate.

Table 2 Total sample and response rate

	Response	*Total Sent*	*Response Rate (%)**
Health authorities	9	11	82
Acute trusts	11	15	73
Acute & community trusts	7	8	88
Community & mental health trusts	15	17	88
Ambulance trusts	6	8	75
GPs	6	30	20
Royal colleges & professional organisations	9	14	64
CHCs	10	19	53
Voluntary organisations	16	58	28
Trade unions	0	2	0
TOTAL	**89**	**182 (= 100 per cent)**	**49**

* *All percentages rounded to nearest whole number.*

The focus groups

This part of the research, which consisted of a series of focus groups with clinicians, managers, primary care staff and patients, was conducted by Social and Community Planning Research (SCPR), on behalf of the King's Fund.

The aims of the focus groups were to:

- explore awareness and knowledge of the Patient's Charter among patients
- obtain views of the Charter from clinicians, managers and patients based on their experiences with it
- explore the impact of the Charter from the perspective of these groups
- generate suggestions from each of these groups as to how the Charter should be revised, particularly in the light of their experiences with it.

Focus groups were chosen as the most appropriate means of gathering information because they are open-ended, provide a useful forum within which people can share views and experiences, and are a particularly effective method for 'brainstorming' and generating ideas about improvements. They also gather a range of viewpoints over a short time and the breadth of experience provides a solid base on which to build further research.

Although interactive in nature, each group was conducted with a topic guide to ensure that a similar series of topics was included in every discussion. These were all tape-recorded with the permission of those attending, participants were assured of confidentiality and anonymity in our analysis and reporting of the data.

Ten focus groups were conducted during November and December 1997, five with patients, two with NHS managers, two with clinicians and one with primary care staff.

Sampling

Patients

In order to obtain as wide a range of views and experiences as possible, patients were selected according to: age, gender experience of the NHS in the year previously either by themselves or as a carer, and the nature of their NHS experience. People were excluded from the groups if they were employees of the NHS or private health care providers lest they influence the views of others.

A screening exercise was carried out during late October and early November 1997 in five NHS regions to select people with recent experience of using the NHS. The study areas comprised a mixture of urban and rural, as well as places with different socio-economic profiles.

The screening took the form of an explanation of the nature, purpose and sponsor of the study and those willing to take part were then asked a short series of questions about themselves and their recent experiences of the NHS. Quotas were assigned for each of the four main sampling factors and recruiters were instructed who to invite to the focus groups to ensure that each included people with a range of experiences. All members of the public who answered these questions were given a letter giving details of the study, reassuring them of confidentiality, and including contact information if they had any further questions. Those invited to a focus group received a letter with details of the time of the group and the local venue in which it would be held. Copies of the screening questionnaire and letters to study participants are available from SCPR.

As age was expected to be an important factor in people's experiences, views and priorities for health care, each group was banded within a broad range of 18–45 (two groups), 46–65+ (two groups), and mixed ages (one group).

In total, 36 people were included in the patients' focus groups. A payment of £15 was given to each patient who took part in order to cover time, travel or childcare costs (see Table 3).

Clinicians, primary care staff and NHS managers

Four NHS regions were chosen for the random selection of professionals: Northern and Yorkshire, North and South Thames, Anglia and Oxford, and North West.

There were five focus groups for managers and clinicians: two for managers from acute, community, ambulance, mental health trusts and health authorities; two for clinicians and nurses from acute trusts, and one for GPs, practice managers and nurses from the primary care sector.

Recruitment was initiated through the chief executive or senior partner of the organisation who recommended an appropriate candidate. Only one trust approached declined the invitation to send a representative. Approximately 70 per cent of the GP practices approached wished to send a candidate but were unable to do so due to pressure of work and/or lack of a fee.

Chief executives, directors of quality, complaints managers, nurse managers, ambulance managers and Patient's Charter managers were recruited for the managers' focus groups.

Table 3 Profile of patients attending the focus groups (Total number of participants: 36)

Age		*Sex*	
18–25 years	3	Male	14
26–45 years	11	Female	22
46–64 years	13		
65+ years	9		
Personal experience of the NHS in the past year *			
Travelled to or visited by a GP			34
Inpatient experience			15
Outpatient experience			28
Attended an A&E department			10
User of community services			10
Day case patient			4
User of maternity services			1
Experience as a carer in the past year			
Experience as a carer			12
No experience as a carer			23
Non-response			1
Employment status			
In paid full-time employment or self-employment			14
In part-time employment			1
Unemployed			2
Retired			14
Unable to work because of illness/disability			2
Looking after children/relatives			3

* Patients were asked about all of their recent NHS experiences. The total number of different types of experiences therefore exceeds 36 as some patients had more than one type of experience.

Consultants and ward sisters were recruited from the A&E, orthopaedic, obstetrics and gynaecology, psychiatry, general surgery and cardiac departments of acute trusts for the clinicians' groups. It proved impossible to recruit junior doctors. General practitioners, practice managers and practice nurses were recruited from both fundholding and non-fundholding practices, with other representatives from total purchasing projects.

Table 4 shows the distribution of staff across different functional areas.

Table 4 Profile of NHS staff attending the focus groups (Total number of participants: 62)

Managers	
Information/quality/performance managers	8
Service managers (general & operational)	17
Service managers (clinical)	15
Primary care managers (e.g. practice managers)	3
Clinicians	
Nursing staff (all grades)	7
General practitioners/GP assistants	5
Hospital doctors/consultants	7

Analysis

The analysis was carried out using the Framework method developed by SCPR's Qualitative Research Unit. It involves charting data from the transcripts in a synthesised form into a series of thematic matrices to allow easy comparison between and within cases. All of the data from the transcript is systematically condensed and categorised in this way.

Copies of the topic guides and the questionnaire used for focus groups and the written evidence are available from the King's Fund.